Kelly's OIL

MY HEALING WITH CANNABIS

KELLY NOAH HAUF

MILLICHAP BOOKS

Edited by Christine Booth

Cover and text design by Carl Brune

kellyshealingpath.com and kellysoil.com websites
    by Robert Millichap

Cover photo by Jillian Hauf

Back cover photo by Rick Hauf

ISBN 978-1-937462-47-5

millichapbooks.com

To my grandparents, Paul and Edna, and to my granddaughters, Joliet and Jerra

CONTENTS

Prologue vii

Tumor Is Back 1

The Great Adventure 5

Colorado 13

San Francisco 21

Ceremony 33

Search for Answers 37

Regimen 39

Protocol 45

Ninety-day MRI 49

Family Reunion 55

420 61

Verdict 63

Oklahoma 67

Yuma 79

Emerald Triangle 83

FECO 93

Success 95

Epilogue 101

Gratitudes 103

Oklahoma Passes SQ788 109

What I Did 113

Recipes 118

Resources 125

About Kelly's Oil 127

It was January 2000. I had the worst headache I had
ever had. I often experienced headaches, but the intensity of
this headache was extraordinary, so painful I could not even
move my eyes. All I could do was lie on the bed and hold my
head.

After a few hours of excruciating pain, my husband, Rick,
helped me to the car and drove to the walk-in clinic. He
insisted I get an MRI or CT scan because something must be
very wrong to have a headache this severe. Rick was an EMT
as well as Assistant Chief of the Stillwater Fire Department
so the clinicians knew him and trusted his assessment.

They performed a CT scan and gave me pain medication.
The scan showed what the clinician said looked like a one-
inch round mass on my left frontal lobe. He recommended I
see a doctor as soon as possible and schedule an MRI.

I saw tears welling up in my husband's eyes. I was
stunned—not that anyone looking at me could have seen
much emotion on my face. I typically respond to stress by
holding back as if not feeling the emotion would change the
actuality of what was happening.

We immediately scheduled an MRI in Stillwater. My
mother, Paulette, who lived in San Francisco, flew in for the
procedure. As she, Rick, and I sat in the lobby waiting for
the results, I kept thinking about my two daughters. They
were young teenagers. What would I say to them? I could not
imagine telling them their mom had a brain tumor and might
die.

When the doctor called us in, we looked at my MRI while he outlined with his pen what was quite clearly a mass the size of a ping pong ball on the left side of my brain.

"It's very accessible," he said. "That's good, and it might even be a cyst."

I finally started to breathe again. The doctor went on to say he was not that worried, but just the same, he referred me to a neurosurgeon in Oklahoma City for another opinion.

The neurosurgeon in Oklahoma City was not so positive. That doctor thought it was a higher probability that the mass was a tumor and not a cyst. The only way to know for sure was to biopsy it.

"And if we were going to do a biopsy," he said, "we might as well surgically remove the tumor at the same time as many of the risks would be the same."

I was not ready to commit to brain surgery. I asked what my other options were. The ensuing back-and-forth between us was a skirmish of wills–him insisting on surgery, me resisting. Finally, he had me sign a release form stating that I refused his medical recommendations.

A few days later, I traveled to Boston's Massachusetts General Hospital for an appointment with the head of neurology, who happened to be a family friend from Oklahoma. I took my MRI scans and met with the hospital's tumor board. The doctors concurred it was a tumor, but were optimistic that it did not appear to have its own blood supply. In their opinion, it did not need to be removed immediately. They thought it would be reasonable to monitor the tumor closely and, if it started to grow or change, have surgery at that point.

I had an MRI every three months for almost three years after that, and the tumor never grew. For three months I would almost forget I had a tumor, then it would be time for another MRI. I never slept the night before. I had claustrophobia but did not want to take the Xanax doctors usually prescribed. The only way I could get through lying still in that MRI scanner was for Rick to be nearby. He held my foot and calmly and gently squeezed it if he saw I was starting to panic.

It would not be an exaggeration to say that Rick was my hero. He was a fireman and a first responder. When he would see anyone in trouble his first instinct was to go to the rescue. He was often the first person on the scene even when he was off duty. It also meant we were often late to events, still, it was part of why I loved him.

After three years of MRIs showing no change, Rick and I grew comfortable with the tumor that stayed in the background of our lives. I knew most people would want a brain tumor removed immediately. When they learned of my choice to wait their surprise was often quite apparent. For me, however, I was grateful simply to have another day of wonderfully ordinary life with my family.

Then, in 2003 after one of my routine MRIs, I got the news I had feared. The tumor had grown by 25% in the past three months. There was also evidence of a second tumor, a small one, buried in the center of my brain.

At that point, Rick and I agreed it was time to consider

surgery. Mom arranged for me to talk with a San Francisco doctor, whose father also had a brain tumor. He had just compiled research to find the best brain surgery team in the country and recommended that I go to the neurological center at Cedars-Sinai in Los Angeles. We made an appointment the next day.

My two daughters, Jenna and Jillian, had never been to Los Angeles. I wanted them to be there with me when I went into surgery, but I also did not want them to be upset or scared. I thought if we framed the trip as "Yay! California vacation!" it might make it easier for all of us.

By then, of course, the girls knew about the brain tumor. They were old enough to understand it was serious, but, as young teenagers, they were more concerned about suddenly growing taller than all the boys in their classes. Rick and I were nervous, but we distracted ourselves making these days fun and light-hearted ones for our daughters. I kept thinking it could be our last family vacation.

The day of surgery happened to fall on Rick's birthday. My father, Don, flew in from North Carolina, and Mom and my sister, Donna, drove down from San Francisco along with Francis, a family friend.

Francis had the ability to make any event, no matter how onerous, seem like an opportunity to celebrate being alive. He had a degree in psychology and played guitar with a few San Francisco rock bands in the seventies before opening a music store and showcase venue in Petaluma. He was an important resource for instruments and equipment and championed fundraisers for musicians in health crises at his store. Most significant to me, Francis was a gifted medical intuitive. His grandfather had been a shaman from Spain and Francis had followed in his path. Just being in his company brightened my spirits.

When my name was called for surgery, I had to walk down a long hallway and through double doors to the surgical center. My long blonde hair was tied in a braid. Mom said her strongest memory of that day was my braid bouncing on my back as I walked that last distance without her and Rick.

I woke up from surgery to someone repeatedly calling my name. I was freezing, shivering so intensely I almost shook off the gurney. Rick was beside me. He gently put his hands on me to let me know he was there. I could hear him calling out to the intensive care nurses, "She's going hypothermic! I need a warm blanket on her immediately!" They rushed over and wrapped me in a plastic blanket hooked up to a machine that blew warm air into it.

My eyes were still closed as I listened to the medical team chart my vitals and share the surgery results with my family. I felt disconnected from my body. I was floating near the ceiling, looking down at them, feeling as though I could intuit their thoughts without the need for words.

The surgery had gone smoothly and the results could not have been better. The neurosurgeon reported a total resection, in other words, a removal, of the large tumor on my left frontal lobe. No attempt was made to remove a smaller tumor that the doctors had already concurred was inoperable. The team was pleased with the results and did not recommend any follow-up chemo or radiation. The news was just what we had hoped for, and, although I still felt like I was watching the scene from high above, I was elated.

The odd sense of disassociation lingered for several days of my recovery, but my vanity managed to plant itself firmly on the earthly plane. I wanted to see what my hair looked like. I had been concerned they would have to shave my head. Luckily, Cedars-Sinai was in Beverly Hills where vanity runs deep, so the surgical team had been very sensitive to my concern. Still, they had shaved a one-and-a-half-inch strip across my head from ear to ear. My sister had already rushed out to Rodeo Drive to buy me several beautiful scarves to cover the scar.

A few days later I was released from the hospital and we rented a lovely suite nearby where we spent several days while I recovered. At last, I returned to Stillwater and resumed my life. MRIs were still required every three months because of the second tumor and because of the tendency of tumors like mine to grow back.

My tumor was a Grade II oligodendroglioma, a type of tumor of the central nervous system that grows slowly and is usually benign. If the tumor starts to grow, left untreated, it can pressure surrounding brain tissue leading to very undesirable outcomes like seizures, migraines, blindness, inability to talk or walk, even death. After surgical removal, oligodendroglioma tumors have a high rate of recurrence within three to ten years. They tend to grow back in a more aggressive form and often increase in grade over time. Grade III tumors grow quickly and usually, if not always, contain cancer cells.

TUMOR IS BACK

It was early December of 2013. My husband
Rick and I were having dinner at Eskimo Joe's in our
hometown of Stillwater. Oklahoma State University students
congregated around the long bar toasting the end of final
exams, their raucous celebration nearly drowning out the
country music playing on the jukebox.

I had just left the table to wash my hands, weaving
between young servers balancing trays of hamburgers on
one hand and plastic cups of beer on the other, when I felt
my phone vibrating in my pocket. Seeing that it was my
neurosurgeon at Cedars-Sinai Medical Center, I headed
straight out the restaurant front door. Anticipating the
gravity of this call I took a deep breath.

My doctor came right to the point. "Kelly, we've studied
your last MRI, and, unfortunately, it shows a recurrence of
your brain tumor."

I shuddered in the cold night air. As stunning as it was
to hear Dr. M's words, I was not surprised. I had grown
increasingly suspicious that something was not quite right
because of recent changes in my sense of smell. Since my
first surgery ten years ago, I had belonged to an online brain
tumor support group and had heard similar stories. I also
had witnessed firsthand the high frequency of recurrence,
usually within the first two years after surgery.

Dr. M told me that the neurological team recommended I start chemotherapy immediately. Another surgery might also be necessary.

I knew what he was going to say before he said it. It was all too familiar. I had heard it many times from my support group. I had watched them endure debilitating chemotherapy, multiple surgeries, and radiation. The stories almost never ended well.

Dr. M had delivered the bad news and presented his best medical opinion. Then he asked how soon I could arrange to begin treatment.

Long seconds ticked by in silence. My head was buzzing, I couldn't think clearly, but an intuitive resistance staunchly blocked any thought of accepting the treatment Dr. M recommended without question.

Finally, I asked the world-renowned doctor, "Would it be irresponsible if I said no to chemo?"

There was yet another silence. I sensed exasperation.

"No," Dr. M said at last, "How you want to proceed is your choice, Kelly."

I thanked him and said I would discuss it with my husband and get back with him. I stared past the bare trees and street lights at the sliver of the moon. I was so disoriented I might as well have been standing up there. Now, a decade after my first tumor surgery, the other shoe had dropped. For ten years, everything had been fine. Now, things were not fine.

As I walked back inside the restaurant I saw Rick wave at me from across the room with one of those "where have you been?" looks on his face. Moving toward him, I knew the next chapter of my struggle with brain tumors was about to begin.

Rick was right in front of me, standing up, pulling out my chair, looking concerned.

"What is it, honey?"

Thankfully, after I told him the bad news, Rick did not press me for a decision about what I was going to do. All I said was that I first had to let everything sink in and get through the holidays. I needed to watch our granddaughters open their presents.

THE GREAT ADVENTURE

The onset of weird scents leading to my suspicion that my brain tumor was back had started about four months earlier. Over the years I had heard several patients from my group talking about episodes of suddenly smelling all sorts of strange and powerful odors. We soon learned these were olfactory seizures caused by their brain tumors.

My seizures came on at night and would wake me up with a strong acrid smell like urine. My young granddaughter sometimes stayed over and, at first, I thought maybe she had peed in the bed. Twice I got up and changed the sheets, but the strong odor persisted.

My doctor had prescribed Keppra for the seizures, but I was hypersensitive to most medications and resisted taking it. I had read that it could cause explosive anger in some people and there were stories among my support group that confirmed emotional side effects.

I had already begun researching natural remedies to anti-seizure medications and chemotherapy and was excited to read about a natural alternative, cannabis, that could possibly help manage seizures. Most impressive was the story of a little girl with severe epilepsy named Charlotte Figgy. Her mother took her to Colorado Springs to obtain cannabis oil from specialty growers, the Stanley Brothers, who were cultivating a particular variety of marijuana to manage seizures in young people.

From the time Charlotte was a few months old she experienced as many as three hundred grand mal epileptic seizures every week. She was six when she received cannabis oil treatment. Her seizures plummeted to one or two per month. In honor of her remarkable recovery, the brothers renamed their oil "Charlotte's Web." Her story was featured in a 2013 CNN special by Sanjay Gupta.

As I dug deeper into the studies, I found information that suggested cannabis could kill brain tumor cells. A study by a molecular biologist at the Universidad Complutense in Madrid, Spain, Dr. Christina Sanchez, discovered that tetrahydrocannabinol (THC), the primary psychoactive molecule found in the cannabis plant, could systematically wipe out cancer cells. Her work was expanded by Dr. Manuel Guzman, who conducted the first clinical trials on THC's anti-tumoral action in human beings.

It was a tiny study but Guzman injected THC directly into brain tumors of nine patients with glioblastoma tumors. The cannabinoid caused significant reduction of tumor cell growth in all nine people. In yet another report, this one from Harvard University, scientists reported that THC slowed tumor growth and significantly reduced the ability of the cancer to spread. One remark in particular in the report caught my attention that compared THC to a heat-seeking missile that selectively targets and destroys tumor cells while leaving healthy cells unscathed.

The more I learned about cannabis, the less traditional paths of tumor treatment appealed to me. It was known that conventional chemotherapy indiscriminately damaged cells in the brain and body. A very small study from the University of California-San Francisco showed that the chemo drug that had been recommended by my neurosurgeon could kill tumor cells but leave intact the stem cells that could regrow the tumor in an even more aggressive form.

I continued my research as Christmas approached but planned to delay any decisions until after the holidays. After all, I kept thinking, this could be our last Christmas together. I wanted it to be festive and joyful.

My daughter, Jillian, now twenty-six, flew home from San Francisco on Christmas Eve to spend a few days. My older daughter, Jenna, lived close by with our two little granddaughters, Joliet and Jerra. We had a lovely Christmas morning breakfast and opened our gifts. Everything went as beautifully as I had imagined.

After a few hours, Jenna took the children home for naps while Rick, Jillian, and I cleaned up the holiday aftermath. Jillian was our daughter who could always be counted on to be logical, reasonable, and speak her mind.

It was fitting that she straightened her shoulders and blurted out, "Okay, when are we going to address this elephant in the room?"

The question took me by surprise. The family knew about the recent report from Cedars-Sinai but I certainly did not want to discuss my brain tumor on Christmas Day.

"What are you going to do?" Jillian asked, visibly anxious. She was a planner, a woman of action who liked to stay a step ahead of the game.

I tried to gather my thoughts. My voice trembles when I'm

nervous so I didn't want to talk yet. I poured everyone a cup of hot spiced cider and sat down at the kitchen table. The weight of Rick and Jillian's anticipation forced me to begin.

"I am not going through another brain surgery. I'm going to try medical marijuana instead."

Hearing myself say it out loud shocked me as much as it obviously surprised my now wide-eyed husband and daughter. I didn't know until that moment that I had made up my mind and was going to go through with it. And now, I, the upstanding Stillwater, Oklahoma grandmother, was telling my youngest daughter that I was not going to follow the recommendation of the best doctors in the world and instead would be trusting my life to an illegal weed.

Hearing my decision, Rick and Jillian sat in uneasy silence for a few moments. Rick finally got up and started massaging my shoulders. We had briefly talked about cannabis treatment but I could tell he was dazed by my resolution to try it. Jillian began pacing.

Up until this moment my husband and I had been dead set against our children, grown or not, using marijuana. They would never in a million years let us know if they had ever tried it, and the thought that I would even say the word marijuana in the house in front of my children somehow felt wrong, even criminal.

The Stillwater Fire Department had a very strict drug policy and Rick was in charge of testing. He regularly conducted random checks for drug use and anyone testing positive for marijuana or any other illegal drug was fired on the spot. Rick's brother also happened to be the county sheriff and had previously been a drug enforcement officer.

In Oklahoma, marijuana was illegal, even for medical use. We were part of a very conservative community in a very conservative state that boasted some of the most punitive marijuana use penalties in the country. Possession of negligible amounts was punishable with a prison sentence that could span years. Caught selling it, you could spend the rest of your life behind bars.

The State of Oklahoma went so far as to file a lawsuit directly with the United States Supreme Court against the State of Colorado that demanded key portions be stricken from the voter-approved measure allowing adults in Colorado legal access to regulated marijuana. The Court refused to hear the argument, but such was the climate of cannabis acceptance in my state at that time: slim and none.

It was Jillian who at last broke the silence. Not surprisingly, she already had a plan.

"Okay, how about this. What if I cancel my return flight, and instead you, Dad, and I drive back to San Francisco. We can go through Colorado on the way and find out more about Charlotte's Web and then go on to San Francisco and see what people know there."

I expected Rick to dismiss this idea out-of-hand. He wouldn't like it. Jillian's idea was too sudden, too spontaneous, too risky. There wasn't nearly enough preparation in place. There wasn't even enough solid evidence of cannabis's effectiveness to gain his support. Not even close.

"Let's do it," he said.

Jillian and I looked at each other in shock. Soon enough, however, we were hatching this adventurous idea with bubbling excitement. No ball and chain of practicality weighed us down that Christmas night.

Later Rick confided that he thought we were going to Colorado and California to get some information, maybe load up on brochures. More accurately, he thought we could both use a trip. Oklahoma winters can be cold and icy, and the image of a California beach was enticing. Work was stressful and he had built up a lot of vacation time. He knew we definitely needed to move forward with my care even though he was highly skeptical about cannabis as medicine. At this point though, he was willing to pursue anything to support me.

Since Colorado was the closest state to us with legal cannabis, we decided to make Colorado Springs our first destination. It would be near enough to Oklahoma that I could come home often if I could get treatment there. In addition to treatment for my brain tumors, I also wanted to investigate medical marijuana as a way to address my olfactory seizures and headaches.

It felt like a new future of adventurous unknowns had settled atop the mad activity below. We had crossed a threshold and were now on a new path. Christmas morning seemed such a long time ago.

Jillian sat on the edge of our bed as I tore through my closet. She called this my pre-travel ritual. Deciding what to pack has always been difficult for me. I am a survivalist by nature. I'm not comfortable unless I have an arsenal of supplies to assist us through my laundry list of "what if" situations.

This particular packing ritual was especially difficult because how can you prepare for the unexpected when you're traveling into the unknown? I didn't know how long we would be gone or whether we would be spending more time in the snowy mountains of Colorado or the warm beaches of California. Sweaters and wool socks or light linen pants?

Jillian plugged in coordinates on her iPhone GPS with a notebook in her lap. She was charting our path to Colorado Springs while tracking a blistering winter storm that was building to the north. I held up a hat.

"Yay or nay?"

She glanced up. "Yay. You'll want that for the beach."

Satisfied with the route in place, Jillian tapped her pen on her knee. "What should we call it?"

"Call what?"

"This experience. This trip. Any adventure of this magnitude deserves a proper name."

I stuck another black sweater into my suitcase. "How about 'The Great Adventure'?"

"Perfect!" Jillian said writing "The Great Adventure" at the top of the page in cartoonish bubble letters. "The Great Adventure has begun!" she declared and snapped her notebook shut.

"Take it all," Jillian said, watching me second guess another sweater. "The Great Adventure will require all of your favorite clothes. Pack the entire closet!"

While Rick and Jillian filled an ice chest for the trip, I slipped back into my bedroom for a quiet moment alone. I picked up our family portrait from the nightstand and held it to my chest. How could I leave my daughter behind to raise two children? My eyes filled with tears realizing I could miss Jerra's first step.

I took a deep breath and slid the photo into my suitcase.

It was late when we finally took the ornaments off the Christmas tree. Rick and I dragged it down the hill from our house to the side of the unpaved county road. The air was crisp and bright stars filled the sky. It was the sort of night we might have soaked in the hot tub and picked out constellations or built a big fire in the pit. Instead we held hands and walked in step back up the hill.

Coyotes howled in the distance. We didn't know then that it was the last Christmas we would ever spend at our little house on the prairie.

COLORADO

The next morning we were up early and on the expressway heading west. Jillian was curled up in the back seat trying to sleep. Rick turned to me and lowered his voice.

"I really think California made this medical marijuana thing up so it can skirt the law and just get high. I'm sorry, but that's what I think."

I patted his hand and didn't say anything. Of course he would think that coming from the ultra-conservative place where he was raised. A good thing about Rick is that, although he thought we were on a fool's errand, he was willing to go anyway and give it one hundred percent. He would do it for me and for the girls with a couple of weeks in beautiful San Francisco as icing on the cake.

Right on schedule, we approached the blizzard. We began dodging road closings and snow as we made our way in the general direction of Colorado Springs. We were lucky that my friend Janelle had recently relocated there, and when I called she happily invited us to stay at her house while we conducted our research.

I also had another friend who had relocated to Colorado Springs from Stillwater. She was a big supporter of medical marijuana and had purchased and converted a house into a refuge for people who left their illegal states to come to Colorado for cannabis treatment. By giving people a temporary local address, she helped them comply with the current Colorado laws for medical status.

She offered me a room for my entire treatment if I decided to pursue cannabis therapy and insisted my stay would be free of charge. She never charged anyone staying with her for anything. She operated with donations to keep up with the bills. Her bravery and generosity really touched me as she allowed complete strangers to stay so they, or typically, their children, could access cannabis treatments for seizure disorders.

Individuals in Colorado were very generous, but finding cannabis treatment options was very difficult. We didn't find anyone willing and able to tell us what variety of cannabis might be best for my situation. The parents were also having trouble finding someone to guide them. They were positive this treatment was going to help, but, like us, they didn't know where to start. They didn't know what varieties of cannabis existed or which would be best for their child. They didn't know what kind of dosage to take or what strength to take or how often to take it—all the things anyone taking medicine needs to know. None of that information was easily available. They were basically, like us, on their own.

The scant information into cannabis protocols and many tight-lipped resources were a result of the federal government's 1970 Controlled Substances Act. The law declared cannabis a Schedule 1 drug and defined it as a drug with no currently accepted medical use and high potential for abuse. It was difficult to pursue research or obtain funding on a controlled substance. It was also difficult to get a patent on a natural plant that grows wild, leaving pharmaceutical companies little financial incentive to study it. Obviously, no one wanted to risk imprisonment or losing their license by talking to strangers from out of state.

I had grown up with bad press for drugs in a campaign that lumped cannabis with opium, cocaine, heroin, amphetamines, and all other potions of the devil. It was the day of TV public service announcements like "this is your brain on drugs" as an egg drops into a sizzling skillet.

But I also remember growing up spending my summers in North Carolina with my grandparents. It was after one of those sizzling egg ads that Granny told me her parents, my great grandparents, had grown hemp, which was just like the marijuana plant minus the part that made you high.

My grandfather thought hemp was the reason we won the Revolutionary War. It was used for rope and all sorts of things but, most importantly, it was used for making and repairing the canvas sails of big ships. In fact, the words "canvas" and "cannabis" are derived from the Latin meaning "made of hemp." The British required all the original colonies to grow hemp for the mother country. Then during the Revolutionary War, the colonists cut off their supply. The British could no longer repair the sails on their royally dangerous ships and, consequently, we were able to win the war.

Both my grandparents thought it was too bad that hemp got tangled up with cannabis. Even worse was the government throwing the baby out with the bathwater by making it illegal in North Carolina to even grow hemp.

"Shoot," Grandpa grumbled, "Betsy Ross made the first American flag out of hemp!"

During my crash course on all things cannabis, I learned that it has been used for thousands of years—as early as 7,000 B.C.—and by many cultures in India, Egypt, Africa, the Middle East, South America, and later Europe. The Chinese used cannabis in the treatment of over a hundred illnesses. In the U.S., it was a widely accepted medicinal herb in conventional medicine as late as the 1940s.

Cannabis is one of the world's most complex plants with well over 400 active molecules. During the 1950s and 60s promising research flourished in the U.S., Canada, and Europe into demonstrating its ability to successfully treat a number of maladies, including epilepsy, chronic pain, clinical depression, addiction, anxiety, migraines, and schizophrenia.

Research came to an abrupt halt with the 1970 law. Not only in the United States, but in a movement that swept the world, the plug was pulled on cannabis research—not for medicinal reasons, but primarily because of social concerns.

It made no sense to me. It took my breath away just thinking about all those wasted years when we could have been studying and treating pain, illness, and disease with this freely growing, remarkable plant. I didn't care who should have been doing research or why they weren't doing it. I just knew here is a plant with potential for huge medical breakthroughs that grows wild in Oklahoma ditches that had been outlawed because of misguided, uninformed politics and fear.

In the meantime, our Colorado Springs experience grew

increasingly frustrating. We didn't have a medical marijuana card so we were limited in our ability to talk with people working in dispensaries. Someone there might have been able to give us guidance or information or at least pointed us in a promising direction. At last, Jillian convinced us to pack up and move on to what we hoped would be more fertile ground in San Francisco.

Rick drove while Jillian and I continued our research on our phones. Internet reception was spotty and we were both irritated. I was even having trouble locating the previous studies I had found.

One researcher in particular I was looking for was David Meiri, PhD from Israel. My earlier notes said he and his group had been able to get cancer cells to "commit suicide" and that he was more or less duplicating what the Sanchez group in Spain had done. I had taken the time to write out one of Dr. Meiri's quotes: "One of the characteristics of cancer cells is their ability to evade the cell's mechanisms of death, and it seems cannabis somehow succeeds in putting this mechanism back into operation, even if the researchers still do not understand how."

I tried to get back to the source, but nothing came up. I was beginning to feel nervous and fearful, but I didn't want to let Rick or Jillian know I was disheartened. I reminded myself about that gut feeling I'd had—what we needed to know was out there.

When I had more than one bar on my cell phone again I reached out to our friend Francis. I told him we were on our way to California to try medical marijuana treatment for my brain tumor. I needed to hear him tell me what I was doing wasn't reckless.

As always, Francis was calming and positive. He assured me that seeking to cure my tumor with cannabis was a reasonable idea. He gave me the name of a medical marijuana doctor in Sebastopol, Dr. H, to contact for an initial prescription of cannabis when we arrived. He also gave me some information and web links to Dr. A, an oncologist and former head of the University of California-San Francisco Oncology Department.

Most important to Rick, Francis had given us the phone number of a friend of his, John, who had actually cured his throat cancer with cannabis. Given Rick's skepticism, he wanted to talk to a real person who had directly experienced healing with this plant.

We were out of the mountains now and finally had a strong wifi connection. We spent the next fourteen hours watching YouTube videos. We heard doctors explain what happens when cannabinoids from marijuana enter the human body. We listened to Dr. A's recordings that discussed how cannabinoids are a perfect match for receptors CB1 and CB2 in the body's endocannabinoid system. I was amazed to discover that we *have* an endocannabinoid system, referred to as the ECS. I hadn't heard of it but I'm sure I wasn't alone since it had only been scientifically identified in the 1990s.

All the same, it was an enormous scientific discovery. Turns out the ECS is the major homeostatic regulator of the human body, of all animals in fact. It keeps virtually every bodily function in balance and plays a significant role in recovery from every human disease.

Although the cannabinoid receptors are found throughout the body, the brain has more than any other organ. One of the receptors' jobs is to activate a natural process of programmed cell death, also called apoptosis. Apoptosis is necessary in the life cycle of all cells to maintain homeostasis in the body. Cancer cells, however, do not die a regularly scheduled death and rapidly multiply causing tumor growth. Studies show that several cannabinoids, such as THC and CBD, induce apoptosis in malignant cells by acting on the cannabinoid receptors.

Such astounding discoveries to digest as the scenery of Utah flew past my window!

Jillian was in the backseat studying the huge road atlas that she had insisted we buy at a truckstop during a long stretch without GPS.

"You know," she said, "if we take just a tiny detour we can visit Canyonlands National Park before we stop for the night."

We were nearing the exit and Rick quickly changed lanes and flicked on his turn signal.

"The Great Adventure continues!" Jillian cheered.

Our family was determined to transform any journey into a vacation whenever possible just like we had done in Los Angeles all those years ago.

SAN FRANCISCO

We arrived late afternoon as the last rays of sunset were shimmering across the water. The view of the bridge against the skyline was breathtaking. I felt the excitement build as we crossed into San Francisco.

Jillian yelled out from the back seat, "Look at the lights! We're crossing just in time to see them come on."

The Bay Bridge was twinkling and street lights flashed on as we threaded our way through neighborhoods of Victorian houses, busy shops, and packed cafes.

Jillian lived near Golden Gate Park and shared a house with six other people, two of whom were her cousins. Space was tight. Jillian and her fiance, Travas, generously insisted on giving us their bedroom which meant they would be sleeping on floor pallets in the common living area. Everyone had to walk through this space and privacy was nonexistent for them. We knew we were imposing, but we figured we would only be here a few days.

My sister, Donna, owned the property and her son, my dear nephew, Bryan, managed the house. He lived on the second floor with his cute little pug, Molly. He threw his arms around me and assured me he and everyone in the household was excited we were there and would do everything possible to support us.

Bryan was a fabulous cook and, on our arrival, prepared

an incredible meal to welcome us. It was one of the most memorable of my life. After dinner, he played *Méditation from Thaïs* on his violin.

Bryan bought and traded valuable musical instruments, mainly violins, in the States and Europe. His extraordinary talent and art, however, was making and repairing bows. He sold his bows to concert violinists around the globe, and he repaired the bows for the San Francisco Symphony.

During one of our first days here, the entire household loaded up a Radio Flier Wagon with a picnic and went to Golden Gate Park. We spread our blankets at Hellman Hollow where a wide and perfectly manicured lawn lined by magnificent trees sloped gently towards the ocean.

The morning was warm and sunny. We made our way toward a majestic cypress tree with its lower branches outreached. The bumpy texture of the bottom side of the branches made them look to me like a grandmother's arms reaching out to give a hug. Maybe I was projecting my own grandmother's loving presence, but I felt nurtured and protected standing there. I could tell this was going to be a special tree for me—the Grandmother Tree.

After spreading out the blankets, immediately everyone took off their shoes and socks and ran out to play frisbee. It looked like so much fun, running barefoot and laughing on this amazing lawn. The easy flight of the frisbee gliding from one hand to the other was so calming to watch.

I'm typically not one to participate since I tend to be reserved and withdrawn, always watching from the sidelines. I could see everyone having fun, but I had too much to worry about. I had to worry for both Rick and myself. And, honestly, I really didn't know how to play.

Rick seemed carefree, fully embracing the present moment, but what if things didn't work out? We had left Oklahoma thinking it was just to explore options, but what if I had to stay in California for weeks to undergo treatment? I always paid the bills. Who was going to pay the bills? Who was going to check on our house? What if I die?

Rick kept insisting I get up and join the frisbee circle. Reluctantly, I finally did. When the frisbee came my way it blew right past me. I ran to retrieve it and threw it as hard as I could toward Jillian. It went entirely in the wrong direction. I tried again and yet again and each time the frisbee went careening off behind me or into a shrub or in the grass two feet away from me. Why was it so easy for everyone except me?

"No worries, no worries," the kids kept saying. Rick tried to "teach" me how to throw it, but I still couldn't get it right. I simply could not let go at the right time.

I went back and sat on the blanket remembering why I didn't want to participate in the first place. I laid back and took a few deep breaths, filling my lungs with the aroma of the Grandmother Tree.

A few days later we were on our hour-and-a-half drive to Sebastopol for my appointment with Dr. H. He had me complete a prodigious amount of medical background information before telling me he thought cannabis could work for me.

Finally we were receiving guidance from a doctor. It felt

like things might be falling into place. No more scattered notes from YouTube videos or researching the internet for long hours every night.

The doctor relayed a story about a baby with brain cancer who was now cancer free after his parents started regularly putting cannabis oil on the child's pacifier. He ended by writing me a recommendation for medical marijuana.

We looked at it and together Rick and I asked, "So, what's the protocol?"

"We don't really know," Dr. H said apologetically, "but I suggest you start small with a drop of oil no bigger than the size of a grain of rice."

He wrote a name on a piece of paper, "Look up this guy on the internet—Rick Simpson. And when you go to a dispensary ask for FECO or Full Extract Cannabis Oil, sometimes referred to as RSO oil."

"Which dispensary?" I asked.

"Well," he said, "We can't really recommend a dispensary, but Harborside in Oakland has been around a long time so maybe they will have it."

We left with the golden ticket—a cannabis recommendation. I was now officially a medical marijuana patient in the state of California.

Rick was looking up cannabis dispensaries on his phone before we got out the door. Harborside would require us to drive across the double-decked, mega-laned Bay Bridge into Oakland. We were novice city drivers and it seemed too far away with way too much traffic. We decided to try a dispensary in San Francisco.

As we drove, I looked up Rick Simpson on the internet. He was a cannabis cultivator and activist. In 2003, he was diagnosed with basal cell carcinoma skin cancer. After reading a study from *The Journal of the Natural Cancer Institute* in which Tetrahydrocannabinol oil was found to kill cancer cells in mice, he set about extracting his own oil from homegrown cannabis plants. He applied it to his lesion every day for seven days during which time the skin cancer completely disappeared.

Now a true believer in the power of cannabis oil, he shared his discovery with the world—Rick Simpson Oil, known as RSO, or as FECO, for Full Extract Cannabis Oil. It was a thick, greenish-black, tar-like substance typically sold in a syringe at the dispensary.

The Rick Simpson protocol called for ingesting the oil starting with a portion the size of a small grain of rice. After that the dose should be gradually increased by doubling it every four days to slowly build up tolerance until reaching one gram per day. The goal was to consume sixty grams of FECO within ninety days.

I had to be a resident of California to fill my recommendation which meant I had to surrender my Oklahoma drivers license and get a San Francisco ID card. It seemed a bit extreme, but at last I was all set to visit my first ever dispensary.

I had to show my new ID and a doctor's recommendation just to get past the security guard at Sparc Dispensary. I was then greeted by an associate who handed me a sheaf of papers to fill out to become a member of the "club." Most of it was informing me of the law and asking me to check boxes on each tenet that I understood and agreed to. I read every line carefully. I also went through a process to make Rick my caregiver. In case I was not able to personally pick up my medicine he could get it for me without having to become a California resident. That was important since he was still employed by the Stillwater Fire Department.

The dispensary was much fancier than I had imagined. The waiting room had nice leather furniture, chandeliers, and a large leather-bound menu with pages of cannabis items we hadn't a clue about with names like Bubble Gum Kush, Sunset Sherbert, and ACDC. We were given a calendar with free events and meetings scheduled throughout the month for members of the club that included yoga, support groups, and acupuncture.

The dispensary itself had a look of formality with long rows of well-lighted glass display cases full of shelves neatly lined in tinctures and large glass jars of marijuana flower. I sheepishly approached the counter, barely able to look the dispensary employee in the eye.

I asked for FECO oil. No one in the dispensary had it. The young man helping us suggested a high THC tincture but we left empty handed.

Jillian was waiting for us outside. We flashed our sleek membership cards to her as if we were VIPs. She laughed and snapped a group selfie in front of the dispensary sidewalk sign. "For the family history book," she said, "Your first dispensary visit."

We drove to two more dispensaries in search of FECO

with no luck but finally bought an oil that was suggested at the third stop. It was 0.25g of concentrated cannabis oil. It was in a tiny pot, not in a syringe as had been recommended.

Although I had never taken anything like cannabis oil, as soon as we arrived home, I decided to start the process. I was careful to take a tiny dose no larger than a grain of rice. I put it on an almond and popped it in my mouth. We didn't prepare past that or do anything special. I didn't think much would happen.

I thought wrong. The dose was small, but for my tolerance level, it was extremely powerful. I ended up having what I called uncontrollable muscle jerking or maybe more appropriately referred to as an adverse reaction.

I felt like I was in a tunnel. I could hear people talking around me, but I was disconnected from them. At the same time I felt a heightened sense of awareness. Everything was intense. Then I felt like I was floating in open space.

At first the sensation was pleasant, but what had been a gentle drift began to speed up toward something I sensed was big and powerful. I panicked. This was too fast! I didn't want to fly through this tunnel. I back-stroked in the air fighting against the flow. I thought I might be dying.

"Am I dying?" I may have said aloud or it might have been just in my head. I heard Rick talking with my sister, Donna. He must have called her since she is a nurse. She wanted to get me to the emergency room.

I, however, was now having my own conversation with a voice in my head. It was telling me that I wasn't dying. I heard multiple voices saying they were trying to restore it. I managed to say "Wait. Restore what?"

I felt frightened and alone. I had heard about near death experiences where some entity—an angel or a spirit guide—comes to guide you.

I asked the voices, "Are you going to send me an angel?"

A voice said matter-of-factly, "Oh, we sent you an angel many years ago."

"Who? Who's my angel?"

"He's right there beside you. Rick is your angel," the voice said.

Instantly, I understood. Rick had always been devoted and right by my side since we met over thirty years ago. Even now he was sitting on the edge of the bed with his hand on my head.

"Tell him you understand he's your angel," the voice said.

I tried, but I couldn't make a sound. I thought I might be preparing to die, and I desperately needed to tell him how much I loved and appreciated him, but I was in a very different reality. I kept struggling, trying to speak and finally blurted out, "You're my angel!"

Hours later, I was back to the self I recognized.

That I turned out to be super sensitive to cannabis was quite sobering. From this point forward it was critical to build up my tolerance very gradually. Rick asked me repeatedly if I still wanted to continue cannabis treatment.

Most importantly that night, I realized that cannabis was serious medicine even though I didn't understand what that meant. It is difficult to express just how profound this realization was. I sensed a huge, palpable power in this plant.

Though my first experience had been bizarre, it had, all the same, further solidified my trust in its ability to help me.

The next day I called Dr. H to ask him if it was normal to have muscle jerking, an adverse reaction, or even a mild seizure from taking too much of the cannabis oil. He told me in his twenty-plus years of medical marijuana practice, he had never heard of anyone having side effects like I described.

This was not the first time hypersensitivity had been an issue for me. In fact, it was the rule, not the exception. I was even sensitive to over-the-counter pain relievers like aspirin.

I set up an appointment with Dr. A, who I'd listened to in several YouTube videos on our drive to California. As one of the nation's foremost specialists in integrative medicine and cancer treatment, I wanted to meet him and get his medical opinion on integrative support for my tumor treatment.

Rick and I went in for the consultation together. I told Dr. A that we had come from Oklahoma to try cannabis oil as a treatment for my brain tumor and hoped he would give us options for other supportive supplements. Dr. A was visibly surprised we had come halfway across the country to try an unproven cure.

"I can't recommend something like that," he answered immediately. "There is no data supporting cannabis treatment for brain tumors."

His reaction was the first deeply discouraging experience I'd had since setting out on The Great Adventure. His was the voice we had listened to while driving from Oklahoma. His voice was the one that explained how THC targeted cancer cells in the body and caused them to commit suicide.

It was his voice that said cannabinoids are a perfect match to our own endocannabinoid system's CB1 and CB2 receptors creating a state of homeostasis in the body.

Dr. A watched the blood drain from my face. He paused, then stood up and said, "Come with me."

Rick and I followed him down the hall to his office. He handed me a book. "I recommend you read this."

The book was entitled *Marijuanna Gateway to Health* by Clint Werner. He also handed me a brochure about mushrooms with circles around specific ones he thought might help me.

We thanked him and left, feeling somewhat betrayed. The Substance Control Act had made it difficult for doctors to help people with cannabis. They had to be careful, even in California.

My next appointment was with an oncologist, Dr. B, at his office on the UCSF campus. I had already requested that my MRI scans be sent over from Cedars-Sinai. The doctor's assistant asked me to list all the supplements I was taking. I wasn't taking any prescription medicine so that part went quickly. Finally, I told her I was taking cannabis oil and braced for her reaction. She wrote it on my chart without comment or even looking up.

Dr. B came into the exam room with copies of my MRIs. He projected them on a screen for us to compare the last one with the one three months previous.

"Here is the regrowth," Dr. B said. "It's probably the same type of tumor you had removed. These tumors are typically slow-growing, but they do get more aggressive when they grow back. This is quite possibly a higher grade tumor. It is pushing toward the ventricle area. You need to clean it out as soon as possible."

I told him I was trying cannabis oil treatments before I committed to another surgery.

Dr. B looked at me, then looked at Rick, then looked at me again. He was stern and deliberate. "If the tumor encroaches into the ventricle, removal becomes a much more delicate and risky surgery."

"Do you think it would be possible for me to wait three months before committing to surgery?" I asked.

He said it was my decision, but he was going to set me up with a neurosurgeon, Dr. Z, regarded as a master in the field. "He's planning to retire soon, so you should weigh that into your decision to have the tumor out now or risk the wait."

I had heard about Dr. Z from my brain tumor group. He was a nationally recognized expert in treating brain tumors and renowned as one of the most skilled brain surgeons in the world.

Dr. B stood up. "If you decide to wait for your surgery make an appointment before you leave for an MRI in ninety days."

As we walked away down the hall, Rick said, "Well, let's give it ninety days. I still have lots of vacation time built up. I'll call in to the office and tell them we are going to try an experimental treatment not available in Oklahoma."

I could see that Rick was glad at least to have a definite timeline, but suddenly I felt anxious. Ninety days. It didn't seem like much time. Still, if cannabis was going to work at all we might know something in ninety days.

"We don't want to risk another episode like the other day though," I said. "Taking this oil isn't like smoking a joint. This is real medicine and we need to treat it with respect."

I'm not sure at what point Rick was secure enough about the promise of cannabis to begin marching into the treatment protocol wholeheartedly, but our relationship with cannabis had morphed into a feeling of being in the presence of something greater than ourselves.

CEREMONY

I called Francis to tell him about our visit with the
doctors. He had just been released from the hospital after hip
surgery, but he insisted that Rick and I come the next day to
visit him in Petaluma. He said he was on the mend and also
had a friend he wanted us to meet who had cured his throat
cancer with cannabis.

When I told Francis about my first experience with the
oil, he agreed we needed to work with cannabis in a different
way. He said when we came up we would have a ceremony
to respectfully meet the Supreme Mother Cannabis Plant.

When we arrived at Francis' house, he was in his garden.
A curl of smoke from an herb Francis said was copal rose
from a large shell sitting in the center of a Peruvian blanket.

He invited Rick and me to sit on the ground and smudge
ourselves with the smoke of the copal and then sit quietly.
After a few minutes he opened a big pouch of marijuana and
took out a small leaf to put on the altar. He added another
pinch of leaves to burn as an offering to Pacha Mama, the
Goddess revered by the indigenous people of the Andes as
the Mother of Earth and Time and a fertility goddess who
presides over planting and harvesting.

"We ask you, Holy Plant Mother, Daughter, Sister of our
co-evolution in life, to adopt Kelly into your family, to accept
her as your child, as your daughter." Francis looked up at us

and said, "We have an endocannabinoid system within our bodies which means we are deeply related to this cannabis plant as part of our evolution as human beings.

"Kelly, we ask for you to be willing to be adopted into the cannabis plant's world and to have another loving mother along with your human mother. We ask for this plant to see the courage in your heart and to know that you are willing to be true to yourself."

In my heart I answered yes.

"Your relationship with cannabis is now the great and wonderful presence of life affirming life, of life healing and caring for life," Francis continued.

He instructed Rick and me to eat a small bite of the cannabis leaf as a communion with Mother Nature. He then took the leaf on the altar and carefully put it into a beaded necklace envelope, rolled up the beautiful Peruvian cloth and the pouch of marijuana, and presented them to me as a gift. He asked that I keep my own altar at home and bring new life and color to it. "Sit before it in quiet gratitude every day during your treatment."

He told me the marijuana had been gifted to me by his friend, John. He couldn't be there that day but offered to share his knowledge and this gift to help me get started with treatment.

Francis turned to Rick, "Kelly says when she was in a cannabis-induced vision she was told you are her angel."

Rick laughed with embarrassment. "I'm not so sure Kelly would agree that I am an angel."

"I remember so profoundly from the first surgery, because

I was there at Cedars-Sinai with you guys, how huge your love for Kelly was and how deeply you felt it. It was so powerful. It was angelic. It was indescribable just to see that opening of love and connection. I believe there is an angelic presence in life that supports us and helps and guides us, and that we can be in a relationship with that love.

"Rick, Kelly is going to need that kind of support on this journey. Kelly, let Rick guide you in learning how to live in the present moment and become one with the flow of life."

The ceremony cemented the shift to our emerging attitudes of cannabis as powerful, sacred medicine. Rick and I knew we had to start over. We promised to approach everything we did carefully and with reverence.

I know it might sound ridiculous and a strange thing to say about what most people saw as just a plant, but I began to feel that cannabis wanted to help me, had even chosen me. I didn't understand it or how to express it, but I knew this plant would help me. I knew if I listened carefully, she would guide me where I needed to go. I needed to trust in her, in the process, and follow her wisdom.

SEARCH FOR ANSWERS

We continued our search for the Full Extract Cannabis Oil the doctor in Sebastopol had recommended, but none of the dispensaries we visited had it. We still didn't know what I needed to take regarding the ratio of THC to CBD, short for cannabidiol—the non-psychoactive cannabis chemical. Rick said he thought it needed to be over 70% THC, but another article said it was supposed to be only CBD. It was very confusing.

We spent the next two weeks trying different ratios. I had an adverse reaction to the high amount of THC every day, but these reactions were never as overwhelming as the first one. We quickly realized we didn't know enough and couldn't find out enough, quickly enough, to make this experiment work. We searched for guidance everywhere. We heard about a cannabis support group in Santa Cruz that was the first and longest operating cannabis cooperative in the country named WAMM (Wo/Men's Alliance for Medical Marijuana). Rick found a number and gave them a call.

The woman who answered was one of the founding members of the group and seemed confident cannabis oil might cure a brain tumor. She told Rick the process for joining the cooperative was to go to Santa Cruz and meet her and the group, and then to sign up to help in the gardens on a daily or weekly basis. Once we were part of WAMM we could purchase their pure organic cannabis oil. Rick said he was okay with all of that and when could we meet everyone?

She said, unfortunately, they were full and weren't accepting applicants. She invited Rick to try again in a few months as people sometimes dropped out. Needless to say, we were crushed.

After a couple of weeks experimenting with different combinations of THC/CBD cannabis products, Sparc, a local dispensary, finally got a shipment of FECO (Full Extract Cannabis Oil). We couldn't get there fast enough. It was as if the Holy Grail had arrived.

It was very high in THC but contained almost no CBD. It came in a syringe. We were excited to finally have in hand the FECO product that Dr. H had initially suggested, but we still didn't understand what ratio of THC to CBD would be best for me.

At nearly the same time, we received an email from Francis' friend, John, with links to several documentaries on healing with cannabis. One of the links was *Run from the Cure* by Rick Simpson.

Obtaining the right form of cannabis oil was just one prong in the fight against my brain tumors. We were avidly working to revamp our total lifestyle. Diet, sleep, exercise, strong relationships, and a calm sense of being–all are key in regaining or maintaining optimum health. I came to realize that we can treat our problems, but ultimately it is the body that must heal itself.

Fully nourishing and sustaining my body in the best condition as well as I could was my job now. I sometimes thought about what a great change this was. With my first brain surgery I had turned over complete control of my life to the surgical team. I was so passive. I followed orders. How different now with the reins firmly in my hands. It may sound like a small thing, but taking responsibility for my own health was ground-shifting.

In the countless sources we read, the one thing all research adamantly agreed upon was the vital importance of a clean, healthy diet that would work synergistically with any healing regimen. One of our most important guides were books by Dr. Andrew Weil and his recommended food pyramid.

I only reluctantly admit that our Stillwater diet was chock full of greasy hamburgers, french fries, milk shakes, and sodas. Our meat-centered meals were typical of this part of the country. For us, those days were over.

We were lucky to be in a city that highly prized its homegrown organic food. We joined what the household agreed was the best grocery store co-op in San Francisco called the Rainbow Grocery. Inside was an incredibly lush spread of beautiful, fresh, locally grown, all-organic fruits and vegetables. There were exotic teas and fresh herbs and almost any supplement known to humans. We found all the mushrooms suggested by Dr. A—cordyceps, reishi, maitake, mesima, royal sun blazei, lion's mane, chaga, and turkey tail. I took enzymes and prebiotics and probiotics to support my digestion and gut microbiome. I looked into Laetrile, also known as B-17, which could reportedly kill cancer cells. I found out I could get Laetrile from apricot pits. The body converts Laetrile to cyanide and too much can kill you. I was meticulous about how much I took, carefully calculating the dosage according to my weight.

Donna gave us a Kangen water machine that turns tap water into alkaline drinking water. Rick installed it in the kitchen, and we used it for all drinking and cooking. If there was a hint of an appliance making food or water healthier to ingest, we were game to try it.

The mother of Cassandra, one of our housemates, came to visit from Hawaii. She was a clinical psychologist but was also a Kahuna, a traditional Hawaiian healer. She introduced me to olena, a root we know as turmeric. She suggested I start taking it every day so I added it to my daily routine.

Rick bought a powerful juicer and became devoted to it. He juiced carrots, broccoli, kale, ginger, beets, celery, and turmeric root and whatever other fruits and vegetables were in season at the time. We drank Rick's powerhouse concoctions every day. He'd pour us both a glass and we'd offer up a toast to our progress in becoming the healthiest versions of ourselves. As the drink went down my throat I would immediately feel better, like I was taking in the force of life.

As often as I could afford a professional massage, I had one. My cousin, Karla, another housemate, was a practitioner of Reiki, a Japanese form of energy healing. She worked on one chakra point per day concentrating on opening and energizing the free flow of energy, or "chi," throughout my body.

Another aspect of my healing ritual addressed emotional and spiritual issues. I had been listening for a few weeks to a spiritual leader named Panache Desai. His words spoke to my heart. He had just written a new book so I ordered and read it. It provided a guidebook for releasing emotional trauma through thirty-three sessions designed to be done consecutively, one each day. I devoutly did this work.

I also practiced creative visualization. A webinar on the subject given by Lisa Nichols suggested writing a script about what I hoped to achieve on my healing path. The script, she said, should include all of the five senses—vision, taste, smell, touch, hearing—in my scenario. Here is the scenario I wrote:

I follow the nurse into the patient room. As I walk into the room I can smell the antiseptic clinical environment. I sit down in a chair and feel the chair beneath my back and legs. I reach out my arm so the nurse can take my blood pressure and I feel the squeeze of the blood pressure cuff. I stick out my hand to get my oximeter reading and feel the clip on my fingertip.

The doctor walks in. I stand up to greet him, shaking his hand. I feel the pressure of his palm touching mine. The doctor sits down at his computer and opens my MRI to compare it to the previous one.

Rick and I look over the doctor's shoulder as he describes what he is seeing on the MRI. We can see both MRIs, the before cannabis treatment and the after cannabis treatment. I see a tumor in the before scan. On the after scan I see a perfectly clear brain free of tumors. The doctor tells us the great news: the tumor is gone! We are outrageously excited and thank him profusely. We leave and give each other a high five as we walk toward the elevator.

Every morning before getting out of bed I visualized this script.

And then there was physical exercise—one of the most important aspects of healing for anyone. Rick and I took daily walks in Golden Gate Park. At first I could only go a short distance before I would have to rest, but soon I could walk all the way to the ocean. I gradually worked up to making it all the way to San Francisco's famous Cliff House on the beach and finally all the way back through the park to the Grandmother Tree.

I could never have done the work without Rick. By this time I was taking so much THC I was not able to do many ordinary things on my own. He was my anchor. I doubt if I could have kept going if not for his unrelenting determination. It would have been easy to lose confidence navigating a world we knew nothing about just a few weeks ago.

PROTOCOL

As was clear by this time, the cannabis cure was dense
with challenges. We still couldn't find well-defined road maps
or protocols for treatment. I was still having mild adverse
reactions almost every day and occasionally even mild
uncontrollable muscle jerking. I was always afraid I would
have one of these episodes in public with people around
staring at me. It was bound to happen, of course. While at
one of the many weekend festivals we attended in Golden
Gate Park, I felt one of these episodes coming on.

It was so crowded we could barely turn around. Rick
quickly led me to a tiny spot next to a shrub. He sat behind
me so I could lean back against his chest, and he pulled
his poncho over me. When the episode was over, I was too
embarrassed to uncover myself. I finally peeked out the side
of the poncho to see kids right next to us swaying inside their
hoola hoops. No one was paying the slightest bit of attention
to me.

These adverse reaction episodes remained a problem,
but gradually we began to understand how different
combinations of strains of cannabis and ratios of THC to
CBD caused different reactions in my body. I took FECO
every two hours. Rick started injecting the oil into empty gel
capsules which made it easier for me to take. For the most
part, we followed Rick Simpson's protocol, which prescribed

taking one gram of FECO oil per day. We steadily increased my daily dosage, but because of my THC sensitivity, I still struggled with a fraction of the recommended amount.

We set the alarm for six every morning so I could take my first dose, then I went back to sleep for a couple of hours. When I awoke, I took another dose before drinking a glass of Rick's veggie juice that he batched fresh every other day.

By ten o'clock, Rick had his backpack stuffed full of food, water, and blankets. I had ingested enough oil by this time that I was anxious and had to move—I *had* to move—otherwise, a sense of panic started to accelerate. So we walked.

We usually walked four to six hours every day until I could calm down. We visited the Grandmother Tree every day. I sat beneath her, closed my eyes, and waited until I sensed the grandmother power radiating from above and below.

In March, Rick called UCSF Radiology and scheduled my next MRI appointment for April 14. We tried to have my records of the 2003 brain surgery transferred from Cedars-Sinai only to find out records like ours were destroyed after ten years. It was just days past ten years.

We had copies of some of those records at home so I called Jenna and asked her to go over to the house and mail them to me. We, of course, had the recent MRIs.

We finally had an opportunity to visit John, who had cured his throat cancer with marijuana. John told us in addition to taking FECO, he liked to eat the fresh bud. I told him I didn't like the taste, so he suggested we pack it tightly in an empty gel cap so I could just swallow it.

It turned out to be a brilliant suggestion. Rick used a chopstick to pack the ground flowers that were high in CBD into gel caps. This greatly reduced the psychoactive effect of the THC for me and the fresh flower added cannabis in raw form which was a great addition to the FECO I was already taking.

It had taken ninety days to piece together what seemed like a viable protocol for me. We both wished I could have avoided those earlier-day high levels of THC that knocked me for a loop, but we hoped our experimentation would someday help other people avoid such pitfalls on their medicinal cannabis paths.

NINETY-DAY MRI

In early April, I booked Easter holiday flights to San Francisco for my daughter, Jenna, and her two little girls, Joliet and Jerra. They would be here for Jerra's first birthday. I was so excited to see them, but I worried that we didn't have a double stroller or a car seat for the girls. I knew we would be walking a lot during their stay. How could we manage without a stroller?

I was also worried that I was taking too much THC to be fully present when they were here. I was now taking a half gram of FECO a day.

For three months I had stuck to my new lifestyle practices religiously. The healthy habits I had been practicing became routine. I woke up with the sun without relying on my alarm clock. I was familiar with the neighborhood locals and greeted fruit vendors at the farmers' market by name. Things were easier, and I sensed myself feeling even a bit playful at times.

Despite the pressures of my experimental treatment, I savored with an immense sense of gratitude life's little moments, most of which occurred in the heart of the household—the kitchen. Some of the most heartwarming memories of my life are held in that kitchen. As it is living in one house with several adults, there was always activity in the kitchen.

One afternoon I heard pots banging and my niece, Kat, and daughter, Jillian, giggling with Bryan through my bedroom wall. I came to join them to find Jillian wearing a tomato stained apron and belting the lyrics of *Bobby McGee* into the handle of a spatula singing along with Janis Joplin blaring from the speaker. Bryan kept the beat while stirring a bubbling, rich bolognese sauce on the stove top. He noticed me in the doorway and without disrupting his rhythm he poured me a splash of red wine and nodded at Jillian to pass it to me. The song never broke for a second as his pug, Molly, and Kat's poodle, Margo, kept time with their bouncing tails.

How was it that I was fighting for my life but having fun doing it?

Sometimes I forgot to worry about my brain tumor and our life back in Oklahoma. Sometimes as we walked through the park I practiced throwing the frisbee at Hellman Hollow beside the Grandmother Tree. Sometimes my toss caught the flow and sailed.

Meantime, the scheduled date of my next MRI drew near and I felt my anxiety starting to mount. To take my mind off it, the weekend before the procedure, we invited our new friends, John and Donna, to drive from Santa Rosa to spend the weekend with us. They arrived on Saturday, and we all went to dinner at one of our favorite neighborhood restaurants, then went to Cobb's Comedy Club to watch a show. It felt wonderful to laugh.

At home later that evening we started a fire in the fireplace. Bryan came down and played the violin—this one a Stradivari that had recently come under his care.

The next day after breakfast we all went together on our usual hike down the path through Golden Gate Park to the ocean. After putting our feet into the freezing Pacific, we laid out a blanket and Donna and I sat and talked while John and Rick threw the frisbee. Then we hiked up Land's End, a trail along the bank of the Bay overlooking the Golden Gate Bridge. It was a beautiful weekend with great friends that succeeded in distracting me from thinking about the MRI the next day. That night I was exhausted from our weekend excursions and, fortunately, went right to sleep without my usual fit of worry.

The next morning I woke up and immediately felt the burn in the pit of my stomach that happens without fail when I get nervous. I was always anxious on the day of my MRIs, but this one had so much riding on the outcome. I had left my daughter and granddaughters, left my home, left everything I did and the life I knew. Rick was his usual upbeat and positive self, but I could tell he was nervous, too. He also had put his life on pause including home, family, and a lifelong career.

As we walked from the parking lot of UCSF toward the Radiology Center we looked at each other. I drew a long, deep breath and Rick took my hand.

While putting the port in my arm for the injection of gadolinium that comes halfway through the MRI, my tech told me that her daughter had been diagnosed with the same type of tumor I had. She was curious about my cannabis treatment and prayed I would have a good outcome.

I told her I had not yet reached the recommended

therapeutic dose but was hopeful that I was at least going in the right direction. She stood there smiling at me as I moved into the tube. So many people out there are trying to escape cancer. I hoped what I was going through right now would be able to help others like her daughter in the future. I pulled the cloth over my eyes feeling as if a thousand hopes were pinned to my head.

I still detested having an MRI, but over many years I learned how to better cope with my claustrophobia. For one thing I always had my tech give me a washcloth to cover my eyes. I learned that tip from friends back in Oklahoma who had horses. They always covered the horses' eyes to lead them to places they may not want to go. Like the horses, I did not want to go into this long tube and the cloth helped.

I also always asked the tech not to play music through my headphones. If music was playing I found that I couldn't help but move slightly to the rhythm and staying perfectly still was necessary to obtain the best imagery.

I also found the music distracting, which I guess is the point, but I preferred to meditate. I used the loud banging noises inside the tube to visualize machine guns attacking and killing the tumor cells.

Rick held my foot during the entire process which took just under an hour. He always watched me to make sure I didn't start to fall asleep. If I fell asleep I might jerk and that was very bad for imaging. He also sensed when I started to panic. He squeezed my foot if either happened.

The MRI proceeded smoothly and we immediately left radiology and headed to the records department to pick up a copy of the scan on DVD. One of the top radiologists in the world would read my MRI, but that will take another nine days because of the Easter holiday. Nine excruciatingly long days.

As soon as we got home Jillian and Bryan wanted to see the DVD. We looked at it together on Jillian's computer. I was obviously not trained to read an MRI so I tried hard to detach from my impressions of what I was seeing, but the scans didn't look so good to me.

The MRIs after my surgery ten years ago clearly showed the tumor was gone. It was obvious. In this new scan, I saw what looked to me like the tumor still there on my left lobe. I went to bed early and turned away from Rick so he wouldn't see my tears.

It was April 17, my birthday. Jenna, Joliet, and Jerra were flying in from Stillwater the next day, and I could hardly wait to see them. My friend Terrie was also coming to help Jenna and the children on the plane. I diligently attempted to stay calm and centered as I checked off items on my to do list. We still didn't have a double stroller or a car seat. Rick thought they were too expensive when the girls were only going to be here a few days. I took some deep breaths.

I was very close to my older granddaughter, Joliet. The younger, Jerra, was just a baby when we left Oklahoma. Jenna was a single mom, and the girls had always been a huge part of my and Rick's lives, and we were a huge part of theirs.

One of the reasons I went on this cannabis journey in the first place was so I could live to see them grow up. I was already one of the lucky ones who lived with a brain tumor to see my own children grow up, but I wanted to be here to help guide my grandchildren with a grandmother's wisdom the way my own grandmother had guided me. I hoped I had learned something about life, what it is and what it isn't, and I wanted to share those insights with my granddaughters. I adored being a grandmother.

Rick and I decided we would wait to celebrate my birthday with the girls so we spent the day following our usual routine. We deliberately avoided discussing the MRI, but I silently practiced my creative visualizations. I found it grounding to run through the scene over and over again.

That evening as I walked into our house I saw something had been left at the curb. In San Francisco, people moved frequently and often left good furniture or other things at the curb for someone else to find. I couldn't believe what had been left behind tonight.

It was a double stroller and a car seat. I went into the house and stared out the window. Maybe they were just left for a passer-by. Maybe they were left for just anyone? I couldn't stop staring. There was a double stroller and a car seat practically sitting in my front yard waiting for me to take them! I kept hesitating, afraid to leave the window. At last, I ran out the door and grabbed them.

They were perfect. In seconds, I had the cloth coverings stripped off and in the washer. It was amazing! It was exactly what we needed and exactly what I had asked for.

Rick, Bryan, Jillian, and soon all the housemates came to see what I had. No one could stop talking about the amazing good fortune since they had repeatedly heard my concern about not having a double stroller and car seat while the babies were visiting.

Suddenly, I was questioning everyone in the household and made each swear they hadn't found these things and set them two feet from the front yard so I would be sure to see them. They vigorously denied knowing anything about it. They were so sincere I believed them.

Cassandra said, "You manifested that, Kelly." I was

breathless and overwhelmed with emotion. Maybe the life we were living now actually had made a space for miracles like this to happen.

The next day, it was finally time for the girls to arrive. Rick and Jillian went to pick them up while Bryan and I put together a food platter of Rainbow Grocery's finest.

I had tapered off the cannabis oil since the MRI last week so I could be fully present, and I felt great. That was a particular trait of cannabis that I so humbly and gratefully appreciated—it's not addictive. There are no withdrawal symptoms—it is just over. People can become psychologically dependent on cannabis, and it can be abused, but a human body never becomes physically addicted to cannabis.

We planned quite the celebration. I had adorable little Easter dresses for Joliet and Jerra just like my own grandmother used to give Donna and me every Easter. I had candy eggs and chocolate chicks and cute stuffed bunnies mounded in Easter baskets.

Bryan moved his car so Rick could pull into his space in front of the house and minutes later they arrived. Molly, the pug, entered a state of barking frenzy, and we burst out the door to greet the girls.

My heart sang. I was ecstatic. Joliet was her same, sweet, curious, outgoing self. I had been afraid she would have forgotten me and might be shy, but she ran right into my arms and hugged me first thing before moving on to Molly.

Jerra was tired and buried her face in her mother's arms as Jenna carried her inside. She wasn't crying, but there was no chance Jenna was going to get to put her down or pass her over to her Oma or Opa. I was overjoyed to be "Oma" again.

That night Bryan made an incredible lemon butter Sole Meunière. We had a blast chattering away. Later we went up on the roof. The babies were mesmerized by city lights and Opa's spinning game. Jerra's little eyes sparkled in the light from her single birthday candle when she tried to blow it out. Joliet had to help. It was all so perfectly beautiful up here under the stars, my dear little family back together.

We were up early the next day. The stroller fit both girls perfectly. I was excited to share my daily walk on the path in Golden Gate Park. When we reached the Grandmother Tree, I squatted down by the stroller and told my babies that the outstretched limbs were grandmother arms, always open to them like my own.

Joliet liked this story. We lifted her out of the stroller and she ran under the tree where Rick picked her up and sat her on a limb. Such a smile of wonderment!

We walked all the way to the beach. We couldn't possibly have done it without the double stroller. It was the first time the girls had ever seen the ocean, and they loved it. They exhausted all of us playing charge and retreat in the surf.

On Sunday, I put out the Easter baskets for Joliet and Jerra to find as soon as they woke up. I could hardly wait to dress them in their frilly new outfits. For me, Easter has always been special—the bright new green of spring, budding flowers, new growth, new life, rebirth. I felt reborn in a way. These past three months in San Francisco had been transformative. I was not sure how to express it exactly, but it was as if something inside me had come to life, some new dimension added to what I used to know.

Everything around me seemed exquisitely beautiful. Was it always beautiful? I felt so extraordinarily blessed. The gravity of consciously realizing just how much I had changed overwhelmed me. No matter what happened with the brain tumor, the disease no longer defined my life.

420
April 20, 2014

There was a festival in Golden Gate Park.
Everyone in the house wanted to go. We packed up the Flier
and the crew walked over to what we have heard is one of
the largest gatherings of 420 in the world.

Being from Oklahoma, I had never heard of a 420
gathering. We had to look it up. It was a celebration of
marijuana that happened every year on April 20, hence 420.
It was a quirky little story.

It seemed that back in 1971, five teenagers from San
Rafael, just north of San Francisco, got together at 4:20 pm
under the Louis Pasteur statue that stood near their school.

The brother of one of the five had given them a treasure
map to a plot of cultivated marijuana they could have if they
could find it. The brother was in the Coast Guard. One of
his friends had recently enlisted and had to leave behind his
small crop now ready for harvesting. Here was the map.

The five friends shared a joint and went off to Point Reyes
in search of marijuana treasure. They never found the plants,
the story goes, but had so much fun on the adventure they
vowed to meet every April 20 at the Louis Pasteur statue at
4:20 to enjoy marijuana and think up new treasure hunts.
The group of friends became known as the Waldos and 420,
or sometimes 420 Louis, became code to gather at the wall

61

for a marijuana smoke break.

As it happened, one of the Waldos brothers was a roadie for the Grateful Dead. The band members started using the 420 code and it spread like wildfire among the counterculture. From then on, thousands gathered every year on Hippie Hill in San Francisco as well as other places dotted around the world.

I was curious to see the 420 crowd on Hippie Hill. It was bound to be colorful. By the time our crew arrived, a huge crowd had already assembled on a patchwork of blankets. The scent of cannabis smoke was in the air. Lots of police walked around making no attempt to interact with the crowd. It was a peaceful, mellow group. And colorful, very colorful.

We were lucky to find a piece of lawn just big enough to spread out our blanket. After claiming our spot we took turns exploring. At first I felt uncomfortable bringing my grandchildren into the festival, but quickly saw many children playing and having fun. I took Joliet and Jerra to the nearby playground that not only had swings and slides but also a wonderful carousel. I felt so full of joy playing in the sunshine with my two beautiful young granddaughters. The whole day was sweet. I loved every minute of it.

VERDICT

April 23 we would get the verdict. I had a noon appointment with the oncologist. As we drove to the doctor's office, Rick and I pretended it was just another trip to the doctor. We didn't look at each other much.

I checked in and we sat down in the waiting area, which was framed with a wall of glass and a gorgeous view of the Golden Gate Bridge. I closed my eyes and started visualizing just like I have done every morning for the last few months.

I was still visualizing when my name was called. Rick and I were put in a patient room and the nurse took my vitals just as in my visualized script. The doctor walked in, and Rick and I stood and shook hands. The feel of his hand in mine was so familiar—just the way I had imagined in my visualization. That's good, I thought. So far, so good.

Dr. B sat down at the computer and opened my MRI to compare it to the previous one. Rick and I looked over his shoulder as he described what he saw. To me, the two still looked the same and Dr. B confirmed as much.

"The new scan appears unchanged," he said.

I would have sworn at that moment that someone had just jabbed me in the stomach. My visualization script was veering horribly off course.

Dr. B swung around in his chair to look us in the eye, "This is good news. If you had been on chemotherapy for the last four months this is what we would hope to see."

I straightened up. This was not my script, but I had just heard Dr. B say "good news." A surge of energy powered through me. That part *was* in my visualization. I was back on track. My shoulders lowered about six inches.

"Do you think it would be okay for me to continue the treatment I have been doing rather than chemo?"

"Yes, we can do that," he said. "There has been no change for the worse. We can do another MRI in four months. If you have any adverse symptoms we can always do another MRI sooner than that."

"And what about the second tumor?" I asked.

"What second tumor?" Dr. B said.

Rick jumped in at that point, obviously astounded by the question. "The one in the middle of her brain that was inoperable? The little one. We've been watching that one too."

Dr. B spun back around and examined the scan again comparing the two images back and forth, blowing up different areas with Rick and me breathing down his neck. At last he wheeled around to look at us again.

"I don't see a second tumor in the new scan. Things can appear and disappear in brain scans. What looks like a tumor in the November scan might have been something we call an artifact."

Rick and I looked at each other and knew something was amiss. I'm not sure why we didn't discuss it further with Dr. B, but by this time Rick and I had been around the block a few times. We both knew that years ago the doctors at Cedar-Sinai had done a special test, a spectroscopy, and determined that the second tumor had the same chemical components as the large tumor they removed. The small tumor was inoperable so it had always been a concern. If it started to grow, I would have been in real trouble. Rick and I had watched that second tumor remain the same size for ten years.

We thanked Dr. B and left. When we reached the elevator we looked at each other in bewilderment. Could this really be true? Did cannabis just kill that small brain tumor and arrest growth in the larger tumor? We high-fived.

We went down the elevator and out of the building without saying a word, but there was a tidal wave of emotion swelling in my throat as we walked to our car. Once inside I began repeating "Oh my God!" Tears streamed down Rick's cheeks.

"This is real!" he said, "This is really happening, Kelly! You're going to be fine. You're going to be well."

We hugged so tightly a crowbar couldn't have separated us. Suddenly, Rick took my face in both hands and pulled me back to look me in the eye. His face was lit up like I hadn't seen it since our wedding day.

"I have thirty years in the Fire Department—that's plenty to retire with my pension. Let's go home, sell the house, move out here, and do this."

My head was spinning. "Rick, are you serious?"

"I've never been so serious. Look, this whole experience has shown me that you can pack up and change your whole life. You can move away. You can leave, and you can totally change, and it can be so much better. If I could express that in a way that would encourage someone to see the possibilities in their life, I would feel really good about that."

Here was my husband, the man who had dealt with the daily terror of holding my life in his hands through a world he knew nothing about just a few months ago. The good news today was not just my victory. It was, in so many ways, every bit as much Rick's.

OKLAHOMA

The next few days we were giddy with excitement. We celebrated our hopeful news with family and friends. Jenna and the girls were here for another week so we packed in every fun excursion we could think of. I loved San Francisco, loved our house by the park, loved our housemates and our friends, and, most of all, I loved our family. My heart never felt so open.

My sister Donna and her husband, Peter, owned the house where we were living. When I asked her if we could come back and stay another four months so I could continue treatment, she graciously agreed.

One of our housemates had already made plans to move and soon opened a room for us. I was deeply appreciative of all the sacrifices of space and convenience every person in this house had so cheerfully made for us, especially my sweet Jillian and Travas, who had been sleeping on the living room floor for months now without a single complaint.

The gravity of our big news and big decision was sinking in. Rick had to apply for his retirement from the fire department. Then, we had to get our house ready to sell. We had to pack up everything we had acquired for the past thirty years! Retiring, selling our house and moving halfway across the country to . . . to where exactly after this current housemate situation? It was one thing to talk about this new adventure, it was going to be another thing entirely to pull it off.

I felt worry mounting at my doorstep, but learning to meditate and visualize helped me not only to fight my tumor but also avoid panic attacks and generally function in a more grounded way. Still, this was a big step. All the good news had elevated the last few days, but my confidence felt a bit fragile.

At the end of the week, Jenna and the girls and my friend Terrie flew back to Oklahoma. Rick and I packed our car and left for Stillwater a few days later. We had been away for four months, but it seemed like a lifetime.

We took a small amount of FECO with us. I couldn't afford to let my tolerance drop too much. There was so much work ahead of me and I certainly did not want to give the tumor any opportunity to grow. I had my California medical marijuana card, but I wasn't sure it would protect me from arrest if we were stopped beyond the California border.

I had more than one flare of anger about the state and federal laws that made my cannabis oil treatment illegal. Did I really have to face prison for trying to stay alive?

After a late start, we finally pulled out of San Francisco headed for our overnight destination of Las Vegas. We could find a nice hotel for a reasonable price there, but, who am I kidding, Rick loved to play craps.

We arrived at dusk and checked into the Golden Nugget downtown. We had a delicious dinner and then headed for the casino. Rick had a big time and ended up winning enough money to pay for our hotel room.

We left Las Vegas the next day headed for Williams, Arizona. Our plan was to stay the night there and then head up to the Grand Canyon the next day.

Three years ago on a trip from Oklahoma to California to visit Jillian, Rick and I stayed in Williams so we could take the Polar Express Train on a Grand Canyon Tour. The morning we were to get on the train, the trip was canceled due to bad weather. I had been very disappointed, and the canyon had been on my Must Go There List ever since.

I had seen lots of pictures of the Grand Canyon, but when I got to the rim and looked into that abyss, I burst into tears. It was as if the veil between the worlds had lifted and everything that ever happened was inscribed in this incredible stone depth.

Rick walked out on a thin ledge extending into the canyon. I had read about people falling to their death from the edge. I screamed and begged him to come back, but he just laughed.

We decided to stay in Moriarty, New Mexico that night. It was too late for dinner out when we arrived so we ate what we had in our bag—half a pear with cashew butter and an avocado with rosemary and goat cheese.

The next day we drove ten hours and finally arrived home. It was late, and we were exhausted. Pulling up our long driveway, it was as if we had arrived at the end of the earth. Everything looked simultaneously familiar and foreign.

I remembered the day we moved into this house. We were so happy. Rick took a picture of me sitting fully clothed in the large spa bathtub. I could stretch out my whole body. I remembered us laughing and opening a bottle of champagne for a toast to our family and our life in this new home.

We built the house after Rick's parents gifted us the eight-acre property and my grandparents gave us the down payment. It was going to be our forever homestead where we would raise our children. I wanted it to be like my grandparents' home in North Carolina. I loved it there. I awoke every morning to birds singing and country ham frying. I had planned for this home to be like that for my children and someday for my grandchildren—a place that would always be here no matter what.

Rick had grown up on this Oklahoma prairie and had spent his whole life here. Our house was on a hill and from the top you could see open prairie for miles around. I always thought the clean open lines of the landscape were where Rick got his direct and honest nature. But then again, the prairie was deceptive. The land appeared to be flat with nothing to hide when, in fact, it was full of gullies and folds capable of concealing whole herds of buffalo back in the day.

Rick told me again and again on our drive home just how much he was ready to move on. Ironically, for a fireman, Rick had always been a sailor at heart. He had his sailing certification and had always dreamed of having his own boat or even being a hand on someone else's boat and sailing around the world. I always thought he would have left for the sea many years ago if it weren't for our family.

He didn't really own much or collect anything so I'd always told him that he could move in ten minutes if he had to. I remembered years back when he was commanding a huge prairie fire scene and our whole town was at risk of burning up. Fires were breaking out everywhere. He was able to find one minute to call me and said, "Kelly, I only have a second. If the fire jumps the highway, our house will be in danger. We have no more available firefighters, so I won't be able to send anyone there to help. Grab our important papers and anything you value and get out now." I had the presence of mind to ask him, "What do you need me to grab for you?" He couldn't think of anything, but finally said, "You better grab my gun." Rick just didn't need stuff.

Our house was not particularly big, but now, after occupying a small room in a house with six others for four months, it looked huge. Rick and I assessed the job ahead of us. We unloaded all the stored items in our ten-by-twenty-foot shed into the house for sorting, then Rick borrowed his dad's rollback truck and moved the shed to a piece of land we owned five miles away.

He came back in and took a look at the huge piles of stuff in the living and dining rooms. "Okay, go through it and get rid of everything you can."

I looked back at him in disbelief. Unlike him, I liked my stuff. I was attached to my stuff. I was sentimental. One whole wall had built-in shelves with glass doors displaying Granny's complete set of china. I was so proud of that china and she was so pleased to give it to me. I picked up a plate and ran my finger over its tiny pink and white flowers.

Neither Jillian nor Jenna wanted any dishes they had to hand wash and only use on special occasions. How sad, I thought, that what had so lovingly been handed down from generation to generation was now often more burden than treasure.

Rick left to get the tractor and brush hog to begin mowing. I sat there alone looking at the piles and the china and no longer felt at all sure that I wanted to sell the house. I wasn't sure if I even wanted to go back to California. I missed Jenna and the grandbabies so much. I didn't want to be away from them any longer. My heart hurt.

I had pulled myself together by the time Rick came back inside. He said he saw a hawk in one of the cottonwood trees. A hawk family had been nesting here for as many years as he could remember.

Jenna had never liked the hawks. When she was a little girl she would run outside with her fists in the air when she saw big birds threatening little ones. When they were nesting, the smaller parent birds would take on the hawks and try to protect their hatchlings. They would work together dive bombing the hawk then fly away just before the hawk could grab them in its deadly talons. Jenna would cry and say she hated the hawks. Rick would patiently take her on his lap and explain that wasn't the way nature worked. He told her there was room for all God's creatures.

Temperatures in Oklahoma could be over one-hundred degrees for the whole month of August. I looked at the boxes of photographs I had taken of all the important days of our family's lives. If I put those captured images in a metal storage unit and set that unit in the Oklahoma sun, those memories would melt into an indecipherable block of time.

These pictures gave me a sense of comfort that my life had happened, that Rick and I had loved each other and our children had been happy. I needed those photographs as a repository outside my own fragile memory.

I moved into the living room and began dismantling my altar. I remembered adding each special piece as it came into my life, and now I removed each one and carefully wrapped it with newspaper. As I picked up a large, beautiful crystal, I remembered when Francis had given it to me.

My mom first introduced me to Francis when she lived in San Francisco, back when I first found the brain tumor in the year 2000. Francis had a ceremony for me with this crystal in the center of his altar. At the conclusion of the ceremony, he carefully wrapped the crystal in a Peruvian cloth and handed it to me to place on my own altar. I didn't have an altar then, so I came home and created one around that special piece. I had been adding to it ever since. I really loved having this place to stay close to those things that touched my heart. I put each precious item into the storage container not knowing if I would ever have a special place like this again.

I knew this process of packing up and clearing out was going to take some time. What I hadn't expected was the intense emotional part. I began to feel very alone and empty. Then I had a flash of the Grandmother Tree. I saw her with her huge arms outreached, standing strong in her glory. The sun shone brightly on the carpet of green grass above the sparkling Pacific. I saw myself and Rick under her branches throwing the frisbee back and forth with ease. It reminded me to let go of my illusions of control. Let go of what I thought my life would be and accept what it is. I heard Rick instructing me to aim and let go. Catch the flow.

Suddenly, I felt guilty. How dare I sit here and have regrets over what I thought my future was to be. I was alive. I had hope. Cannabis was working. Everything was going in the right direction. I told myself to trust in the process and be grateful for what you have and stop grieving over what might have been.

After many days of packing up the household items and fretting over what to keep and what to toss, it became apparent that very little of the accumulation was Rick's, and I was running out of time. The volume was overwhelming. I decided to just throw everything I hadn't gotten to yet into bins and take it to the shed down the road.

A few friends came over to help me with the move. My friend Kate knew we had hard water scale in the bathrooms. We had installed a water softener, but it was still a continuous battle with mineral deposits. She arrived armed with a toothbrush and a look of strong intention as if she secretly had been waiting to do this for years. She spent hours scrubbing the bathrooms until they sparkled.

My friends, Lisa and Dana, asked about our hot tub and Rick told them they could have it if they could move it. They arrived in their pickup, and I watched out the window as they hoisted it into their truck bed before Rick could get off the tractor to help them. No problem for those two strong Oklahoma women!

I dismantled my grandfather's clock and took it to my mother-in-law's for safe keeping along with photographs and paintings by two of my aunts and a watercolor by my dear friend, Native American elder Joseph Rael.

Just as I arrived back home, my friends Terrie, Carla, Cath, and Lori showed up to help too. By late afternoon, Rick was collecting wood for a bonfire. Kate, Carla, and Lori ran over to Bad Brad's Bar-b-Que to pick up dinner and Cath and Terrie went for beer and paper plates.

I got in the shower and stood for a few minutes with my eyes closed letting the warm water splash over me. I kept thinking about the bonfire, that it was probably the last one we would ever have here on this prairie. Soon this land and this house would belong to someone else. My Native American friends always said we can't really own the land, and, somehow, that made me feel better about leaving. We never owned this land, we just lived on it for a while and now we would live somewhere else. Maybe we don't own anything, even our own bodies.

When I got out of the shower, I could hear my friends in the kitchen laughing. I was going to miss these wonderful women.

Terrie wanted to know if it was okay if we made the bonfire a Letting Go Ceremony. "I know we all have things we need to let go of."

"What a great idea, Terrie. I'll let go of my brain tumor."

"I'll let go of that guy I thought I wanted to marry," Lori said.

"I'll let go of the idea that I ever wanted to marry," Kate laughed.

"Write it down," I said, opening a kitchen drawer that

used to be full of pencils and notepads. "Oh dear," I cried looking at the empty drawer.

"No problem, we can use this," Cath said, ripping up a paper sack.

Out the window I saw flames dancing in the fire pit. Rick knew what wood to choose to make the fire light and what wood to add to make it bright and what logs to add to make it last.

On the kitchen counter, I saw slabs of ribs and mounds of barbecue piled on platters. Neither Rick nor I had eaten meat for months. I loaded my plate with coleslaw and potato salad, poured a glass of wine, and headed out to the fire pit. Cath had brought her banjo and soon enough everyone was singing.

After a while, each of us walked to the fire, held our slip of paper bag for a moment of silent prayer then threw our intentions into the blaze. Mine vowed to let go of my dream of becoming my grandparents in this house. I watched it curl up and turn black.

We went to bed exhausted that night but neither of us could sleep. The silence of the prairie felt like glass. The sound of a dog barking in the distance spun vibrations around the room that hung in the air softly ringing until the next bark. So different from San Francisco where this isolated bark so far away would never rise above the white noise of a city that doesn't stop for the night.

Rick's voice pierced the darkness. "You remember when the doctor said the tumor was about what he would expect to see if you had done chemo?"

"Yeah," I said, flipping over on my side to look at him lying there on his back staring at the ceiling.

"Well, what he didn't say was how much *healthier* you and your whole body are than if you would have done chemo." He turned to face me. "I mean, just look at you. Your immune system has not been wiped out. The oil and the food we eat have made your whole body healthier. You're running around here like a poster girl of health."

I skootched over and hugged him. "And I can almost throw a frisbee."

"I'm really proud of you sweetie," he said, smoothing my hair away from my face like he does.

YUMA

We got an offer on the house right away and by early June the herculean task of sorting, trashing, packing, and stashing was done. For all of my previous trepidation about selling and leaving Oklahoma, I was now feeling surprisingly free.

We left our driveway for the last time and I fought the urge to turn around and watch our house fade from view. I relaxed back into my seat as we sped past fields of wheat and hay bales. Just as we reached the interstate, "Happy" by Pharrell Williams came on the radio. We cranked it up and sang along. We were finally on our way back to California.

Jillian was in San Diego visiting friends and asked us to pick her up on our way back to San Francisco. I had only brought a small amount of FECO with me and the supply was critically low. Even though it was out of the way, we decided to go through Colorado and pick up more before heading for San Diego.

We made good time and arrived at a dispensary in time to purchase my FECO. Rick also bought a small amount of marijuana flower for a retirement celebration when we finally made it back to San Francisco.

We were on the road again early the next morning and I made a hotel reservation to stay in Yuma, Arizona that night. It wasn't our usual route and I had never been to Yuma. I was glad to have a change of scenery and an opportunity to see this historic town of the Old West.

It was late when we reached the outskirts of Yuma. We noticed an unusual number of state and local troopers and thought there must be an accident or some sort of emergency ahead. We had to get gas so I went inside and asked the clerk what had happened.

He shrugged. "There's always something happening at the border crossing."

"What border crossing?" I asked.

"Can't leave this town without getting cleared at the crossing. People come over from Mexico with drugs and guns and illegals. When they get into the U.S., they try to go across our state line into California."

We were road weary and ready to find our hotel. We fell asleep right away. The next morning I awoke to the sound of Rick typing on his computer with a distressed look on his face.

"What's up?" I asked.

He sat there for a minute rubbing his chin, staring at the screen. "Well, I just found out that there is no way out of Yuma without going through a checkpoint." He looked up at me. "And we've got that cannabis oil in our luggage."

I jumped out of bed with this revelation. "Can we drive back out the way we came in?"

"No," he said. "It appears there is absolutely no way out of Yuma without a checkpoint. I've mapped every road in all directions."

I stood there a minute before a ray of hope streamed through my mind.

"When I texted Terrie last night that we were headed to Yuma, she texted back that she has a friend who lives here," I said as I grabbed my phone and began searching for Terrie's text. "She gave me his number and suggested we call and meet him. Here it is. Maybe Jack can tell us if there is an alternate route out of town. A dirt road or something only the locals know about."

I dialed his number, and, when Jack answered, Rick took the phone and told him we were friends of his friend, Terrie. Jack said Terrie had told him about us and Kelly's treatment with cannabis and invited us to his home. When we got there, we explained our dilemma.

"No way out of town but through a checkpoint," Jack said matter-of-factly.

"We don't want to throw this oil away when we know it can help someone. Is there any chance you know a person who could use it?" Rick said.

"Well, actually, I do have a friend who has cancer. I'll see if he wants to try it," Jack replied.

We all walked out to get the oil from our car. Rick opened the hatch, located our suitcase, and pulled out the plastic bag from the Colorado dispensary. The lid had worked loose on Rick's small vial of marijuana flower and, as he tipped the bag, the entire contents spilled all over the carpet. The three of us stood there, speechless, staring at it. "They'll have dogs," Jack said.

We brushed and brushed but a lot of the dry marijuana just kept falling deeper into the carpet. We worked on it for a good fifteen minutes doing the best we could. Jack finally wished us luck and we drove off toward the checkpoint.

There was a long line of cars ahead of us. My heart was pounding as we approached our turn at the gate. The dogs were searching every car. It was very hot and just as we pulled up to the checkpoint, the handler in our lane took his dog inside for a drink of water.

The inspector bent down and looked at us through our open window. He had a few questions about our luggage, then he asked "Do you have a gun in your glove compartment?"

My breath caught in my throat. "No," Rick answered truthfully. His gun was locked in a box in the back. The inspector squinted and stared at Rick, then he stared at me. I thought I would have a heart attack at any moment.

At last he waved us forward just as the dog and his handler walked out and resumed sniffing duties with the car behind us.

"We're some kinda lucky," Rick said as I let out a little scream. "Who knew trying to get you well would be so, so . . ."

"So dangerous and scary?" I said loudly.

EMERALD TRIANGLE

We picked up Jillian in San Diego and finally arrived
in San Francisco without further incident. Bryan made
another of his culinary masterpieces to welcome us back and
had invited two of his friends to join the dinner party. They
were beautiful young dancers from Ukraine. When Bryan
played his violin after dinner, they cavorted among us like
graceful gazelles.

It was refreshing to be back among our interesting cadre
of housemates. There was always something happening
that made me smile. Frequently Karla left a tiny bouquet of
flowers in our room or a miniature gluten-free muffin by our
keys.

Bryan's business itself made for some interesting times.
Noticing an opened box on the table one day, I peeked inside
and shrieked when I saw a horse's tail. I jumped halfway
across the room.

"Who has a horse's tail delivered!" I said in disbelief.

Bryan strode into the room and pulled it out of the box. "I
do, Aunt Kelly. I use horse hair in my bows. This is beautiful
music in the making," he said, holding it high as he combed
through the long tail with his fingers.

We comfortably settled back into the company of our
delightful housemates and I resumed the daily rituals of
ingesting my cannabis oil, meditation, half-day walks,

visualization, and beautiful food. For two months everything flowed along without a hitch. Then at the beginning of August, we hit an obstacle.

It was time to buy more FECO but every dispensary in the Bay Area was out. We were told that it was typical for cannabis supplies to dry up from August until the next harvest in October.

We were blindsided by this very bad news. I could not afford to lose the tolerance I had gained—it had been so difficult getting to this level. We had also planned to substantially boost my dosage since my next MRI was set for the end of the month. I had no time to waste.

"I have an idea," Rick said. "Didn't you tell me that our friends back in Oklahoma have a nephew who grows cannabis commercially in the Emerald Triangle? Maybe we could get in touch with him," Rick said with renewed enthusiasm, now that he had landed on a plan. "Maybe he can help us get some FECO, or maybe he has some cannabis flowers he can sell us, and we can just make our own."

Since the 60s, the area of Northern California covering Humboldt, Mendocino, and Trinity counties, known as the Emerald Triangle, had been notorious for its marijuana cultivation. To this day it remains the largest producing region in the U.S. Through decades of illegal growing, secrecy and suspicion had become a cultural way of life there. It was common knowledge that you better know what you're doing when driving around this area or you just might find yourself on the wrong end of a shotgun.

Figuring it was worth a try anyway, I called my friends

back in Oklahoma and told them our situation. They were eager to help and promised to have their nephew, Brad, contact us asap. The following morning, he called. He wasn't at his grow site, which he said was fortunate, and was instead at his home in a little town in Humboldt County. He invited us to drive up and he would sell us some of his last harvest that he had kept for himself.

He gave us the address and said to be sure and get directions beforehand because cell service would go out about thirty minutes before we got there. That was a great tip!

We jumped in the car right away and headed north. An hour later we turned off the main highway onto a smaller road leading into the mountains. It wasn't long before the air was saturated with the aroma of cannabis even inside our car with the windows up.

Rick and I whiffed at each other in disbelief. Any law enforcement officer on this highway could smell it five miles away. We were thrown back to our ingrained fear of police when marijuana was involved. Then we caught ourselves. This was California. Growing cannabis was legal and the growers were now legally cultivating it. Well, probably. Besides, we weren't breaking any laws driving down the highway simply enjoying the gorgeous mountain vistas.

As instructed, I took a few screenshots of our destination map and, sure enough, within thirty miles of the address, we lost cell service. We arrived at a small house on a large lot in a very small town.

Brad came out the door to greet us as soon as we drove up and invited us in to meet his partner, who was eight months pregnant with their first child. Brad disappeared and soon came back with three one-pound, vacuum-sealed bags of cannabis and asked us how much we needed.

"Hey, we really appreciate this, man," Rick said. "We're going to need a pound to make the FECO that Kelly takes for her brain tumor."

Brad was intrigued. He hadn't heard much about cannabis treating tumors, but his own mother was fighting brain cancer. After we told him about the protocol we had been following and the success so far, he was hopeful she would try it.

He asked us if we would like to see his backyard garden where he had a few plants growing. They were astounding, huge, and as tall as small trees, some twelve feet high!

I had never seen anything like it. I wanted to pull out my phone and take a few photos, but thought better of it. I didn't want Brad to have to tell me not to. And I didn't want any incriminating evidence on my phone. Then I asked myself "What incriminating evidence? Cannabis is legal." It is so difficult to avoid falling into a pattern of guilt associated with cannabis, even after all this time.

Seeing our fascination with his garden, Brad said he was getting ready to take some things to his commercial grow site up in the mountains and would we like to see it. We said we would love to.

He packed gear for forty-five minutes until finally running out of room in his truck and asking if he could throw a few things in the back of our SUV. It was getting a little late in the afternoon so we thought we'd take a quick tour and then try to get back to the main highway by dark.

Brad told us to follow him closely because there was no address or way to reach the location by GPS, and then he shot out of the driveway. Rick was a rather slow and careful driver. Trying to stay up with Brad was not for the faint of heart. He was used to this narrow, curvy mountain road, but it was a challenge for us just to keep him in view whizzing around outside curves in the distance.

Then, seemingly out of nowhere, a police car was on our tail, flashing lights and siren on. We pulled over and the officer wanted not only Rick's drivers license but mine as well. My heart was pounding and my hands were shaking as I gave him my California ID. The officer wanted to know what a car with Oklahoma plates was doing up here. Rick explained that we were from Oklahoma but were staying in San Francisco and were just out sightseeing. The officer walked back and got into his car and stayed there for what seemed like way too long.

"I wonder what Brad put in the back of our car?" Rick said.

"Oh great!," I answered. Until then I hadn't given it a thought. Neither of us had a clue what it was. My anxiety was building. For all we knew, he might have loaded a few pounds of marijuana back there.

The officer finally returned with our license and ID card. He told us everyone up here was a grower and they didn't care for strangers much.

"For your own safety, folks," he said, "it would be best for you to move on out of this area."

We thanked him for his concern and drove off as I frantically checked to see if I had cell service so I could call Brad. Nothing. We had no idea where he'd gone. It was getting dark.

"I feel like an idiot for not finding out what he put in the back of our car," I said.

"Oh, no kidding, he seems like a nice guy, but we don't really know him from Adam," Rick said. "And where is he? Heck, where are *we*!"

We were about to give up when we spotted Brad's truck. He immediately got out and unlocked a gate and motioned for us to follow him as he pulled through. Just inside he jumped out and ran back to re-chain the gate. He was in rush mode.

He hopped back in his truck and we followed him up the side of the mountain on a very rough gravel road that grew worse the farther we went. It finally turned into nothing more than a deeply rutted dirt path. It was the kind of road you only tackle in a four-wheel drive vehicle like Brad's, but he kept motioning us on. I was increasingly nervous. How were we going to get out of here tonight and go back to San Francisco? I started taking long deep breaths.

We went through three more chained and locked gates as we worked our way up the mountain. It was clear that we were now at Brad's mercy. With each gate I felt more trapped and vulnerable. By gate three, Rick said he had put us in a bad position here and hoped we weren't in over our heads.

When we finally reached Brad's place it was too dark to see anything. He backed up to the front door of his house and started unloading gear. We did the same and were somewhat relieved to discover Brad had only put some bedding and food in the back of our car.

Unbeknownst to us, Brad assumed we were spending the night and guided us to a small room. He threw a couple of sleeping bags on a bunk bed situated behind a stack of what he said were off-grid batteries for the compound.

It suddenly dawned on me that Jillian had left early for work and knew nothing about our excursion. I knew she would be worried. We thought we would be home by now, but, no, we were on the side of a pitch black mountain somewhere–don't ask us where–at a commercial marijuana field with no cell service and no one knew where we were.

Thankfully, Brad used a different cell provider which he said sometimes got a weak signal if you went outside. He walked out the door with me and handed me his phone.

I called Jillian and she answered cautiously, "Hello."

"Jillian, it's Mom."

"Mom! Why are you calling me from Oregon?"

"We're at a grow in the Emerald Triangle that belongs to some of our Oklahoma friends' nephew, Brad. I don't really know exactly where we are but we're spending the night." I was trying to be brief since I was a bit uncomfortable with Brad standing right in front of me listening to my conversation.

"Wait! What? Why are you calling from Oregon on a strange number?"

I just told her not to worry and I would explain everything tomorrow when I could get cell service again. She was concerned. Yes, well, so was I.

When we went back in, Brad returned to the kitchen and continued cooking. Rick was talking with a couple who lived here at the property, managed the grow operation, and kept an eye on things. Brad served us a remarkable Mexican dinner from a favorite recipe of his. Afterwards, he brought out a plate of his homegrown, beautifully formed cannabis flowers, the pride of his recent crop. We all had a few puffs and chatted a bit before Rick and I went to our bunk bed.

Rick apologized for getting us into this situation. He was wondering if this guy was actually even our friend's nephew. And even if he was, we still didn't know anything about him.

"He seems like a nice guy but how do we know he's trustworthy? People get taken captive and killed for their organs, you know. It happens."

We didn't sleep so well.

The next morning we cautiously emerged from our bed-and-battery room. For the first time we could see out the large picture window a spectacularly breathtaking view. The dense fog line was right under us creating a magical setting for what we could now see was the house perched at the top of the mountain.

Brad cooked us another lovely meal for breakfast and then took us on a tour of his amazing property. It was obvious that years of hard work had gone into creating this off-grid, twenty-plus acre farm. The cannabis plants were, like the ones in his backyard in town, towering "trees" carefully spaced in rows. There were hundreds of them. All were profusely covered in large, intensely aromatic buds, known in the cannabis world as flowers.

We had never seen a commercial grow operation so we were in awe. Brad showed us how he made organic "compost teas" to feed and water the plants. He showed us his greenhouse system and explained how it worked. We walked through the barn where workers, or trimmers, stayed in sleeping rooms during harvest season. He pointed proudly to the brand new processing machine he was eager to install to extract oil from his plants next harvest.

The farm ran on solar power but Brad had also set up a water wheel at a natural waterfall to generate supplemental electricity and funnel water to the plants. There was a large pond on the property as well as big barrels here and there to catch rainwater. All in all, it was quite the impressive operation.

Brad left us to wander around on our own but warned us not to venture off his property because of the bordering "guerilla" grows. A guerrilla group owned the large property next to his, and they were heavily armed. Brad said they would shoot first and no questions would even be asked.

He at last escorted us through the many gates back down the mountain. We bumped along laughing about all our suspicions that had been so unwarranted about the hard-working, ever so kind and hospitable Brad. Organ harvester, indeed!

As soon as cell service reappeared, I called Jillian. She, of course, reprimanded us for our carelessness and lack of responsibility, and she was right. We had taught her well. On with The Great Adventure.

FECO

Safely home, we were eager to tackle producing our own oil. Rick watched several YouTube videos on do-it-yourself FECO and made a list of needed supplies. We quickly picked up all the items on the list. Then went by the liquor store to grab a couple of 90-proof bottles of alcohol for the extraction and returned home to begin the process.

Rick split the pound of marijuana, putting half in one gallon jar and half in another, and then covered all the plant material with alcohol. He sealed the lids and gave them a good shake, which he continued to do every couple of hours throughout the rest of the day.

The next morning he set up his electric skillet on a table on the roof deck. Being a fireman, Rick understood the danger involved in cooking with highly volatile alcohol. This particular method of self-made FECO should always be left to trained professionals with proper extraction and safety equipment. To stay safe, buy it from a dispensary.

Rick carefully planned for every possibility of an explosion or oil fire. It was important to conduct the process in the open air for proper ventilation. He had a fire extinguisher within arm's reach, a garden hose hooked up and ready, along with the lid that came with the electric skillet to smother the fire if necessary. An electric skillet or a rice cooker is often used in this process since an open flame or any arc of electricity, even flipping on a light switch, could potentially ignite the alcohol vapors and explode.

Next, he carefully placed a piece of cheesecloth on top of the strainer, which he set inside the large bowl and poured the contents of the two jars through it. Once the alcohol had drained into the bowl, he gathered the cheesecloth with the plant material inside and repeatedly squeezed it to retrieve as much liquid as possible. He put the plant material aside and took the bowl of alcohol to the deck and carefully poured it into the electric skillet and turned the temperature on very low heat. He donned his fire mitts and began stirring the brew with the heat resistant silicone spatula so as not to create a metal-on-metal spark.

As the alcohol slowly evaporated, the cannabis oil became thicker and thicker until all that remained was a tar-like black oil. After it cooled a little but was still warm, he pulled the sticky goo into syringes which he later used to inject the oil into several empty gel caps.

Rick to the Rescue had done it again, and I was able to avoid any lapse in my treatment and, in fact, we accelerated my dosage. It was a relief to have an ample supply, but Rick and I agreed that we would be very happy when we would be able to simply drive to a dispensary, waltz in, and pick up some cannabis oil.

In the meantime, the days of August ticked by. Before I knew it, I had the cloth over my eyes and my foot safely under Rick's hand as I moved into the MRI tube. Ninety days had passed since my last MRI and now the moment had finally arrived. We were going to find out if our efforts had been worth it.

SUCCESS

On August 30, 2014, two days after my MRI, we went to Dr. B's office to view the digital images. When I saw the scan I could still see something on my left lobe. My heart sank. I braced myself for bad news.

But Dr. B was smiling when he turned to face us.

"Well, Kelly, I don't see a tumor."

"What! What's that?" I asked, pointing to the blob still visible on my left lobe.

Dr. B looked at the scan again. "I suspect what we see on the film is astrogliosis. It's a type of scar tissue and it's left over from your initial surgery, but I can't be sure. The radiology team will evaluate the MRI, and I'll get back with you with the results, but, I'd say, it looks clean."

Rick was effusive with "the best possible news! It's a miracle!"

I, however, was not ready to celebrate yet. I would wait to hear what the radiologists had to say. The blotch on the MRI looked big to me, too big. I wanted to believe the best, but my doubt was unrelenting. I wanted the truth verified in triplicate.

It was a very long two days later, the Friday before Labor Day, when Dr. B finally called. I was outside without my phone. He left a message.

When I returned and saw his voicemail bubble on my

phone, I fell into the nearest chair. No one was at home. I closed my eyes and centered myself. I imagined a great news phone conversation with Dr. B until I worked up the nerve to listen to his message.

The recording quality was terrible. Reception was going in and out and there was an overlay of static. I could pick up Dr. B's voice saying a word or two and then just garbled noise. I heard "radiologists" twice but I couldn't make heads or tails of the rest of it.

My hands were trembling so much I could barely call him back. I got a recording. Dr. B would not be in the office again until after Labor Day.

When Rick and the housemates came home, everybody tried their hand at deciphering the voicemail, but it was impossible.

Rather than spend the weekend in worry and suspense, Rick and I decided to take a road trip with John and Donna to the Rhythm & Joy Festival at Agape Church in Woodland Hills, near Los Angeles. One of the speakers on the program was Panache Desai. Almost every morning for the last six months Rick and I had done Desai's "Receive It" dance meditation. We held our hands high and open to receive a download of positive energy.

The festival was a hoot. John bought special tickets that allowed us to sit under the family tent with the Reverend Michael Beckwith. I met Panache and he autographed his book for me. The four of us danced, we sang, we laughed a lot. Every time I would start to think about my MRI, I jumped up and started dancing again.

The morning of Tuesday, September 2, Dr. B returned my call.

"The news is all good, Kelly," he said. "The radiology team concurred that what we were seeing on the MRI is astrogliosis, not tumor tissue. It looks like, for right now, you're clear."

I was shaking so much I had to lean over the countertop when Rick came into the kitchen. "What is it, Babe," he asked, rushing over to put his arms around me.

"I just heard from Dr. B," I blurted.

Rick was alarmed. "What did he say?"

Bryan just then walked by the kitchen. "Aunt Kelly, are you alright?"

"It worked," I stammered, barely able to get out the words. "It worked, the cannabis worked! The tumor is gone! All that's left is scar tissue."

Rick was hugging me so tightly I could barely breathe. "Hallelujah Kelly!"

We started jumping up and down, laughing. "I don't have a brain tumor anymore!" I shouted to the ceiling.

Bryan had turned white and was still standing there with his jaw unhinged. "It worked? Really, it worked?"

"Jillian! Where's Jillian?" I yelled.

She was already rushing down the stairs.

"I'm cured, Jillian!!"

She was stunned. "What?"

"I'm cured!"

"What?"

"I'm well! The brain tumors are gone!"

"The cannabis worked, Jillian!" Rick said, tears streaming down his face.

The four of us flew into a circle of hugging bodies. Could there ever have been this much joy packed into a single moment? It was a nuclear explosion of joy.

Bryan outdid himself with dinner. We had a hundred toasts and everyone had a story—or three—to share about this adventure.

"I have something for you, Mom" Jillian beamed with excitement as she pulled a small box wrapped with a tiny bow from behind her back. "I was saving this to give you after we heard from your doctor. I thought either way the news went, you would like this to carry with you as a reminder of your connection with . . . well, just open it!"

I unwrapped the tiny bow and opened the box to find a small glass container with a cork on top strung on a silver chain necklace. I held the glass to the light, trying to determine what was inside.

"It's pieces from The Grandmother Tree!" Jillian blurted, no longer able to contain her excitement. "I gathered small pieces of bark and a piece from her leaf and sealed them inside!"

"Oh Jillian! What a thoughtful and precious gift!" I gushed, clasping the chain around my neck. My heart was so full I thought it might explode, and I could not contain the tears streaming from my eyes as I hugged her. It was one of the most meaningful gifts I had ever received—one I knew I would forever wear over my heart.

That night when we finally fell into bed, Rick said "Wow,

Kelly, this has certainly been a Great Adventure! Did you visualize tonight like this?"

"Yes. No. Yes, I visualized it, but not this wonderful. I never could have imagined anything quite so perfect," I said, clutching my new necklace. "Just look at this sweet gift!"

When I awoke the next morning, everything seemed brighter. I jumped up, put on my Grandmother Tree necklace, told Rick to grab his backpack, and, a few minutes later, we both headed out the door toward the park.

Rick found it hard to keep up with my pace. Within minutes, I arrived at Hellman Hollow. I sat down on the fresh cut grass under The Grandmother Tree and took off my shoes.

"Let's throw the frisbee!" I yelled out.

Rick seemed surprised by my playfulness and happily yelled back, "Let's do it!"

I pulled the frisbee out of our backpack and ran in the other direction to gain space between us. I put my attention on the cool breeze on my face and the soft wet grass between my toes. I felt hope, gratitude, and excitement for life like I had never experienced before.

I stood there a minute listening to bird songs, then took a deep breath, pulling in the aroma of the eucalyptus trees. I aimed and tossed the frisbee toward Rick, letting go at precisely the right moment for it to glide smoothly and directly into his hand.

"You did it!" Rick yelled as he jumped up and down and ran toward me for an embrace. "It was perfect!"

I knew, at least in that single moment, I was truly in the flow of life.

EPILOGUE

We left San Francisco and moved east to the Sierra Nevada foothills after accepting an invitation from Tolly Burkan, father of the international firewalking movement, to join him in his next empowerment class.

We lived there for two years participating and helping Tolly and his facilitator Kevin Axtell with world class firewalking and empowerment workshops before buying a house down the road in the winter of 2017.

On June 26, 2018, Oklahoma voters legalized medical marijuana by passing HB788. We sold our home in the foothills and moved back to Oklahoma and started a legal cultivation and processing lab in July 2019. We were excited to finally be able to offer cannabis medicine to cancer patients in our home state of Oklahoma.

While we were busy making cannabis medicine, we found out that Rick's PSA (Prostate Specific Antigen) blood test had gone from a four while living in the mountains to a nine within two years, then up to a thirteen when retested three months later. Due to the Covid-19 pandemic we made an online appointment with a specialist from UCSF who said Rick, with the high PSA score and his sudden drop in weight, had a 30% chance of cancer in his prostate. He recommended a specialist in Tulsa to be closer to home.

While waiting for the appointment, Rick began taking

FECO. He was able to increase his tolerance more quickly than I did and was up to taking a full gram a day within four weeks. By the time he saw the doctor he had already consumed close to sixty grams of FECO. The doctor recommended a specialized type of MRI that would not only detect cancer in his prostate but also detect if it was an aggressive form.

When the results came back, he did not have cancer. We were overjoyed with that news, and we wondered if FECO was responsible again for killing cancer cells. We will never know for certain, but he gained weight and his PSA numbers continued to drop.

During my treatment in 2014 I had to rely on scarce anecdotal evidence, which was inconsistent and often incorrect. Now, in 2022, cannabis has been studied and medical marijuana is legal in thirty-eight states, three territories, and the District of Columbia. A bill has just been proposed to make medical marijuana legal nationally and to declassify it as a Schedule 1 drug so it can be researched more thoroughly.

I still have an MRI once a year, the last one occurring four months ago. All my reports have remained clear and stable since 2014.

GRATITUDES

Helpers on my journey

First and foremost, I want to thank my daughter, Jillian Hauf, for being the one who took my thought of trying marijuana and turned it into a plan of action. Jillian, if not for you, I'm confident that The Great Adventure would not have happened in the first place. I am grateful for your leadership, strength, and enthusiasm. I'm so blessed by your devotion and fierce love for family. Thank you for always celebrating every milestone with me. You are always my first call. Thank you also, for your excellent editing and writing additions to the book, and for being my constant sounding board.

To Rick Hauf, my husband and given earth angel, without your love, support, and devotion throughout my treatment I might not be here to write this story. Thank you for never leaving my side during the tough times. Thank you for always insisting with the radiology techs that being in the room to hold my foot during my MRI wasn't optional. I can't imagine life without your calming strength and playful nature.

To my daughter, Jenna Hauf Martin, thank you for your strength in holding down the fort that year as a single mom with two young daughters. Thank you for always loving and supporting me and sharing my story with everyone you know. Thank you also, for sharing your beautiful, kind, generous spirit with us. You are so loved.

Thank you, granddaughters, Joliet and Jerra, for bringing so much joy to my life.

To my son-in-law, Travas Perry, I am grateful for your consistent generosity and fun-loving, easy-going nature. Thank you for giving up your bedroom and privacy so we could have your space. Your over-the-top generosity is a consistent personal attribute of yours that always makes people feel loved and appreciated.

To my nephew, Bryan Campbell, thank you for opening your beautiful home to us. I am so blessed by your total love and support and for making us always feel welcome. Thank you for keeping us well fed with Michelin quality meals and filling our space with classical violin music. And, of course, for creating the delicious recipe for Kelly's Gluten Free Chocolate Chip Cookies! But mostly, thank you for teaching me about a whole new level of generosity apparent in everything you do.

To my niece, Kat Campbell, for always giving of your love and support.

To my friend and mentor, Francis Rico, for your love, support, and guidance. Thank you for your special spiritual gifts that connected me with the spirit of cannabis.

To my sister, Donna Noah, and my brother-in-law, Peter Lynch, for helping us stay in San Francisco during my treatment. If it weren't for you two, we wouldn't have been able to pull this off.

To our housemate, Cassandra Poggi, for sharing your home and accepting us as Ohana.

To our friends, John and Donna LeCave, for sticking with us through it all.

To my cousin, Karla Dierks, for your love and guidance in energetic healing. Thank you also for sprinkling your thoughtful gifts, instilling delight in knowing I was in your thoughts.

To my brothers and sisters, Dr. Jeff Noah, Robert Millichap, Donna Noah, Leslie Noah Huffine, and Lauren Noah Valentino for always trusting and believing in me without judgment.

To my friend, Terrie Altman, for always being there with me in life. Thank you for helping me write the very first timeline from which this book emerged. Thank you for pounding the pavement gathering signatures and sharing knowledge to help get medical marijuana on the ballot so everyone in Oklahoma now has access to the same treatment I did.

To my girlfriends, Donna Doughty, Kate Swenson, Lori Green, Pam Bellatti, Cathy Fowler, Carla Williams, Marla Stevens, Kim Swearingen, Gwen Parker, Janelle Scribner, Lynn Lansford, and Lisa and Dana Bromley, for your friendship, cannabis activism, sharing my story, and encouraging me to write it.

To my friend, Pete Molesworth, for his consistent encouragement to write a book.

To my friends, Daniel Doughty, Alana and Puddin Payne, Urmas Purde, and Asa and Rolf Beckman, thank you for trusting in me and the medicine.

To, our friends, Harland & Beverly Wells, thank you for

your belief in us. Your trust and support and generosity will never be forgotten.

To Dr. Don Noah, my dad, for your love, trust, and encouragement in me using cannabis medicine, our cannabis business, and writing this book. Thank you, Dad, this means more than you know.

To, Gene Hauf, my late father-in-law, for trusting us enough to try cannabis medicine for your own pain.

To, Jo Hauf, my mother-in-law, for holding down the fort for us while we were away. When we returned to Oklahoma, you were a major player in the daily operation of our business and a huge advocate for cannabis medicine. I can't thank you enough for believing and trusting in us.

To my friend and mentor, Tolly Burkan, for teaching me I can do so much more than I thought or imagined.

To my friends, Michael and Michelle Aldrich, cannabis historians, for having the foresight to collect the world's most extensive library on the cannabis movement through media. Thank you for your relentless efforts for the past fifty years in paving the way for cannabis medicine so people like me have a chance to use it legally.

To the late, Dennis Peron, often referred as the father of medical marijuana, for his relentless work in legalizing cannabis and his profound understanding that all cannabis is medicine and should not be differentiated between medical and recreational.

To Rick Simpson for rediscovering concentrated cannabis oil for treating cancer and sharing that information with the world.

To my friend, Jon Marsh, thank you for sharing information and testimonials about how patients can cure themselves of cancer with cannabis medicine.

To my friend, Corrie Yellin, thank you for sharing your knowledge, information, and guidance about cannabis medicine to patients seeking help.

In addition, I want to offer my gratitude to all the countless supporters of extended family and friends who believed in me and encouraged me along the way. Each positive comment, email, call, message, text, "like" &" love", thumbs up, wink, clap, finger's crossed, prayer and spoken encouragement meant more to me than you will ever know. These large and small gestures had enormous impact on my ability to keep going.

Helpers on the book

Even though I have been credited as the author of this book I had a tremendous number of helpers. Many of whom spent countless hours helping me write, rewrite, edit, edit again, and edit yet again. When I started this book, I had no idea how much was involved in this process. For various reasons, this book has taken me eight years to complete.

First and foremost, enormous gratitude goes to Paulette Millichap, my mom. Thank you for your unconditional love, trust, and encouragement during my choice of treatment. That couldn't have been easy on a mother. Thank you for celebrating each milestone and success with us. And thank you for your commitment to getting my story in print and for sharing your expert knowledge in book publishing. Thank you for taking my rambling words and funneling them into a focused and concise story. Without your herculean efforts I'm positive this book would not have happened. Thank you, mom, for this gift.

To my friend, Christine Booth, for her full commitment of time and devotion to my story. Her extensive editing, restructuring, and rewriting of the manuscript were invaluable.

To my friend, Judith Brooks, for her reading, editing, and guidance on the manuscript, and for sharing her expert botanical formulating skills.

To Carol Haralson and Sally Dennison for their reading, editing, and reediting.

To our designer and friend, Carl Brune for his beautiful cover and interior design work.

OKLAHOMA PASSES SQ 788

JUNE 26, 2018

A letter from Terrie Altman

My dear friend, Kelly Hauf, left her home in Oklahoma to treat her brain tumor recurrence in California with cannabis. I knew very little about the treatment she was choosing, but I respected her right to choose it.

My mother had been a cancer patient for many years at MD Anderson in Houston. She would fly home to Oklahoma from other countries with her big red Samsonite suitcase filled with experimental drugs prescribed by MD Anderson oncologists. Kelly had a doctor's recommendation for cannabis but couldn't come home to Oklahoma to the support of her family and friends.

I've always tried to channel my nervous energy into problem solving, but I was challenged by the fact that Kelly couldn't choose to treat her brain tumor in her own hometown because the medicine she chose to use was illegal in our state. Rick and Kelly could lose everything if she tried to do the treatments in Oklahoma. They could even go to jail. I believed this was a violation of Kelly's rights, but I wasn't sure how to help her.

The end of February I had a phone call from a friend. "There is this meeting next week that you might be interested in attending," she said. That meeting, was with a political candidate in Oklahoma City who was working on a marijuana petition. That petition opened up another petition by Senator Connie Johnson who was working on decriminalization of marijuana as a means of resolving the incarceration issues within the state. There was also a medical marijuana petition from a group in Tulsa. It was coming clear to me that to help Kelly I needed to focus on making cannabis legal.

Two more petitions were brought forward by other groups. Some petitions were brought up expecting to fail but were meant to draw interest or make a public statement of intent. There were a total of five petitions.

Encouraging interest and sharing information for the petitions was a challenge. We utilized various methods of communication since people's comfort level with marijuana was iffy to say the least. I found I had a lot of Facebook stalkers. They would read the discussions and articles I shared of things I had learned along the petition trail. Sometimes the stalkers would slip up and like something and I would be able to see them. Some stalkers would even send me messages and ask questions about activities like where to get more petitions, what the new legislation meant, etc. I knew people were paying attention. I set up calling trees like we had before everyone had cellphones. My group set up trees with a minimum of three people asking them to forward the message to at least three other people when they received a message from me. It was surprising how many responded and immediately forwarded the message. It seemed to be working. People were getting the information.

In the meantime, Kelly arranged for me to fly to California with Jenna and her two young daughters, Jerra and Joliet. I was so happy to be able to see Kelly and learn more about her treatments. Kelly was getting the result of her first MRI scan since starting the cannabis and this would tell us if the treatments were working. Kelly's results were "stable" for the main tumor and a smaller, inoperable tumor deep in her brain had disappeared. Kelly's doctor said he was encouraged enough to recommend she continue the cannabis treatment another four months. We were ecstatic. This was great news and made me more determined to get legalization passed so she could come back to Oklahoma without fear of prosecution. I went home with a new resolve to continue educating the public to the need for legalization of medical marijuana/cannabis.

The collection of signatures was non-partisan. People from all parties wanted legalization. I canvassed Oklahoma City, as others were working various events in their home areas. It was nice to see everyone working together for the cause. I started getting lots of calls and messages asking where the petitions were or what the new initiatives meant. Some people worried law enforcement would use the lists against them and insisted on signing only my petitions. I think they trusted me to keep the petitions secure.

As time went on, people started having open discussions about legalization on social media. Research started being shared to support the various uses of cannabis as treatment. People would send me messages in email because they were afraid of the pot stigma. People were beginning to change their minds. They asked me to vet and then post their comments to FB. People began to trust that more information was coming. Anecdotal research was being shared to support the various treatments for pain, seizures, arthritis, and other diseases and conditions. Recently a faith-based magazine printed that there was data that medical cannabis did in fact decrease opioid usage. The more I shared, the more people were educated.

In September of 2015 Kelly Hauf had her second MRI scan and her doctor confirmed her brain tumors was gone. Her cannabis treatment had worked. The word went out to Kelly and Rick's friends in Oklahoma and many of them joined me in getting petitions signed.

The calling/texting/messaging tree was in place. I kept telling people that if we get enough signatures to get the initiative on the ballot, they had to get out and vote. There were a few of us that were dedicated petitioners. Most of us were older and knew the importance of keeping the momentum going. We would hit the Friday night events that always had a lot of people. First Friday at Paseo, H & 8th, Theatre District, and we almost always had a pop up tent at Meridian and NW Expressway and sometimes at Belle Isle Library. I continued to get petitions and to educate the public on Facebook.

The last petition of 2017 garnered sufficient signatures and Governor Fallin signed off on the initiative for inclusion on the June ballot. It was not a general election but Oklahomans showed up in record numbers. SQ 788 passed on June, 26, 2018 with 58% of the vote.

WHAT I DID

Cannabis Oil (FECO)

I followed the Rick Simpson Protocol of sixty grams in ninety days. I didn't follow it exactly; I listened to my own body and increased the dose as I could. To follow his exact protocol, buy his book or consult the internet for his specific instructions. I now understand that his method of making your own oil is only good if you do not have any other option. It is always best to use cannabis oil that has been tested for contaminants, heavy metals, and pesticides and has the cannabinoid and terpene profile information you need to create accurate and consistent doses. I also learned that I was using a Sativa strain but it is advised to use an Indica. Sativa is more uplifting and Indica is more sedating. Therefore, I needed to walk instead of sleep.

Fresh Juice

Rick made fresh organic juice for us every two to three days. Typically, it was made from organic carrots, kale, celery, beet, ginger, and turmeric root. He would add black pepper before drinking. Since carrots contain a lot of sugar, we limited the amount but still added them. We drank about six ounces of this elixir daily.

Smoothies

I made morning smoothies with all organic ingredients.

Typically, I used vegetable protein, flax oil, ground chia seed, various berries and fruit, maca powder, black seed oil, coconut water, spinach, almond milk, powdered multi-vitamin mix, and sometimes bananas or other variations of organic healthy ingredients.

Teas

I drank lots of Essiac and Green tea. I frequently would add lemon, honey, cinnamon, and fresh grated turmeric and ginger.

Water

I drank alkaline water from a Kagan water machine that changes your tap water into alkaline water. I had heard that cancer can't survive in an alkaline environment. I am not aware if this information has been debunked but I used it for all my water needs.

Garlic

I ate a lot of garlic. I had heard that garlic can kill cancer cells, so I added it to our meals.

Groceries

All our groceries were organic and gluten free. We chose mainly fruits and vegetables.

Meat

We didn't eat red meat but had sustainable-raised fish and chicken occasionally.

Supplements

Vitamin D3 (5,000 mg)

Vitamin B complete complex

Vitamin C

Vitamin K2

Neuro-Mag

Astaxanthin

Omega 3

CoQ10

Boswellia

Bio-Curcumin

Olena tincture

Multivitamin

Probiotic

Chaga Mushroom

Lion's Mane Mushroom

Stamets 7 Mushrooms

Milk Thistle

Selenium

Apricot Kernels

The amygdalin extracted from apricot kernels has been used to create a chemically modified version of B17, also known as Laetrile. These kernels contain cyanide which is poisonous in large doses. It is extremely important follow the correct dosage for your body weight.

Black Seed Oil

I added one teaspoon to my smoothies. I had read a study from Croatia that the phytochemicals in this oil resulted in a 52% decrease of tumor cells in mice.

Sugar

I gave up most sugar but still enjoyed high quality options.

Walks

I walked at least three miles almost every day. I spent time in nature, deep breathing, laughing, taking in beauty, and learning how to play and have fun.

Releasing Emotional Density

I followed Panache Desai's lessons on releasing emotional density through his workbook, *Discovering Your Soul Signature: 33 Day Path to Purpose, Passion, and Joy.*

Hypnosis

I practiced self-guided hypnosis on a regular basis through audio on subjects such as *healing cancer, radiant health, and cultivating positive mental states.*

Creative Visualization

I created a perfect outcome visualization script using all of my five senses—seeing, hearing, smelling, tasting, and feeling. Every morning before getting out of bed, I visualized this script.

These were the main components of my health plan. Before I started trying to cure my brain tumor, I was a just a midwestern mom and oma, living my life on the Oklahoma prairie eating not-so-healthy food. I feel overwhelmingly blessed to have been granted more time with my family and hopefully to help others by sharing my story.

I'm not a health or nutrition expert. New studies are being conducted and new information is coming out every day. I recommend that people always seek medical advice from their caregivers. I also stress the critical importance of careful due diligence, research, and credible sources of information to all persons looking to create sensible health plans.

Rick and I primarily consumed whole foods, protein smoothies, freshly juiced fruits and vegetables, and quick, easily prepared meals. In addition, with most meals we added servings of my homemade sauerkraut and Rick's fresh grown microgreen sprouts.

RICK'S MICROGREEN SPROUTS

Sulforaphane Sprouts
One Quart Mason Jar Method

Broccoli sprouts are known for their sulforaphane content with has been proven to be excellent for fighting cancer. Kale is a lesser known sulforaphane powerhouse. The mix we use combines five sulforaphane-rich heirloom kale and broccoli seed varieties to create this super nutritious and tasty sprouting seed mix.

You will need:

2 tablespoons of Sulforaphane Mix Sprouting Seeds (available online)

1 quart mason jar (you can use a larger sprouting jar if you'd like, just be sure to adjust the seed quantity accordingly. For instance, if you are using a half-gallon jar, you will need 4 tablespoons rather than 2 tablespoons.)

Sprouting lid/screen

Fresh water for soaking and rinsing

Directions:

Courtesy Rainbow Heirloom Seeds: https://www.rainbowheirloomseeds.com/ product-page/sulforaphane-sprouting-mix

1. Measure two tablespoons of Sulforaphane Sprouting Mix into a quart sized mason jar.

2. Cover the seeds with plenty of water and place sprouting lid on the jar. Allow the seeds to soak overnight for eight to twelve hours.

3. In the morning after soaking your seeds, drain the soak water out of the sprouting jar and then give the seeds a good rinse with fresh water. Drain off all water very well.

4. Shake the seeds out a bit in the jar, making sure that they are not piled up against the screen that would prevent good airflow. Rest the jar on its side on a flat surface. Check the seeds after a few minutes to make sure no water is pooling in the jar. If you notice excess moisture, simply tilt the jar over the sink to drain off the water.

5. This mix of sprouts can be a little bit touchy as they're getting started. Keeping the jar in a dark place with good airflow for the first 4 days while the seeds are germinating can help ensure a good harvest. Another option is to place a dark cloth or lightweight towel over the jar during the first few days, being careful not to cover the screen and impede airflow.

6. On the evening of the first day, rinse and drain your seeds again, following the process outlined in the prior step.

7. On each subsequent day, repeat the rinse and drain process twice a day, morning and evening. The key here is to be sure to thoroughly drain all the water out of the jar after

rinsing.

8. On the final day of sprouting, move your sprouting jar to a sunnier location, such as a windowsill. This will encourage chlorophyll development, causing your sprouts to "green up." Make sure this location is not too hot or extremely bright since this can dry out or even harm the sprouts. Greening up your sprouts should only take a few hours at most.

9. The sulforaphane sprouts should be ready to harvest by the seventh day.

10. To harvest, give the sprouts one final rinse and de-hull, if preferred. Be sure to drain and dry the sprouts thoroughly prior to refrigerating. A salad spinner works great for drying the sprouts.

KELLY'S SAUERKRAUT

Yields: 16 servings

Prep time: 1 hour

Ferment time: 1–4 weeks (I like 2 weeks)

Ingredients:

2½ lb. head of organic cabbage

1½–2 teaspoons salt per pound of cabbage (I use Pink Himalayan)

Large mixing bowl

1-quart glass jar

Glass fermenting weight

Fermenting lid

Optional Extras that I add to customize:

Fresh organic garlic, turmeric, ginger, carrots, beets, powdered organic turmeric, ginger, garlic, cumin, black pepper . . . or whatever you would like to add.

Directions:

1. Remove outer leaves of the cabbage head that are damaged and dirty. Reserve an intact outer leaf, wash, and set aside. Cut the head in half and remove the core. Rinse the remaining cabbage well allowing water to flow between the cabbage leaves. Drain well.

2. Tare the weight of the bowl you will be using, then thinly shred the remaining cabbage with a knife (or a food processor) and weigh the shredded cabbage.

3. Calculate the amount of salt needed, sprinkle it over the cabbage, and toss well. Let sit for at least 15 minutes.

4. Hand massage the cabbage for at least five minutes, during time the cabbage will release a good amount of liquid brine.

5. Pack the cabbage firmly into a clean glass quart jar. Pour the brine that was released during kneading on top.

6. Cut a circle the same diameter as the jar out of the reserved cabbage leaf. Place it on the top of the packed-down cabbage. Place the glass weight on top of the cabbage to ensure that it stays under the brine. If the brine doesn't completely cover the cabbage and weight, top off with a 2% solution of salt water consisting of one teaspoon salt per cup of water.

7. Screw on fermenting lid, place the jar on a rimmed pan to catch any overflow, and allow to ferment at room

temperature in a dark place until the kraut reaches the preferred sourness, usually one to four weeks. In my environment, the cabbage ferments perfectly to my taste in two weeks.

8. When fermenting reaches desired stage, refrigerate the kraut.

KELLY'S GARLIC KRAUT

I always customize my recipe and make half-gallon jars of garlic kraut. I don't like my kraut extra salty, so I use 1½ teaspoon salt per pound. After massaging the cabbage, I add garlic—either ⅛ cup whole crushed, 2 tablespoons chopped, or 1 teaspoon powdered.

Customize to your own taste. Rick and I love garlic and the boost it gives to the immune system.

KELLY'S ANTI-INFLAMMATORY KRAUT

At the same time, I also make a half gallon of my anti-inflammatory mix of 1 tablespoon chopped fresh turmeric and 2 teaspoons ground turmeric, ⅛ cup sliced ginger and 1 teaspoon powdered ginger, ⅛ teaspoon ground black pepper, and sometimes I add shredded carrots and/or shredded beets, and ⅛ teaspoon cumin. Again, this is just a guide, customize to your own taste.

KELLY'S GLUTEN FREE CHOCOLATE CHIP COOKIES

(from Bryan Campbell)

INGREDIENTS

¾ cup firmly packed almond flour or almond meal (about 3 ounces or 100 grams)

¼ cup firmly packed coconut flour (about 1½ ounces or 43 grams)

1 teaspoon baking soda

½ teaspoon fine grain sea salt (use ¼ teaspoon if using regular table salt or if you're sensitive to salt)

Dash cinnamon (optional)

½ cup butter or coconut oil, melted

½ cup real maple syrup (preferably grade B) or honey

1 teaspoon vanilla extract

6 ounces dark chocolate, chopped, or 1 cup chocolate chips

1 cup chopped walnuts or pecans. I like to candy them before adding. Add a tablespoon of butter and brown sugar and sauté until toasted and caramelized.

Flaky sea salt

INSTRUCTIONS

1. Preheat oven to 350 degrees Fahrenheit and line a cookie sheet with parchment paper.

2. In a medium bowl, whisk together the flours, baking soda, salt and cinnamon. Pour in the melted butter (or coconut oil), maple syrup (or honey) and vanilla extract.

Mix thoroughly. Stir in the chocolate.

3. Let the dough rest for 5 minutes in the refrigerator so the coconut flour can absorb some of the excess moisture (or let the dough chill in the fridge for 10+ minutes if you want fat cookies).

4. Scoop dough, one tablespoon at a time, in mounds onto the baking sheet, spacing two inches apart.

5. Bake for about 11 minutes, until golden brown. I like to lightly mash them down a bit with a fork about half way through the baking process.

6. Cool cookies on the baking sheet for about 10 minutes, then slide onto parchment paper-lined cooling rack. Dust with flaked salt, if preferred.

RESOURCES

Websites

Cannabis Health Radio
Podcast of personal testimonials.
cannabishealthradio.com/podcast

Cannabis Success Stories
Personal healing stories.
cannabisoilsuccessstories.com/portfolio.html

Granny Storm Crow List
An extensive compilation of articles about a variety of
conditions that reference marijuana and cannabis.
grannystormcrowslist.wordpress.com/the-list/

kellyshealingpath.com

kellysoil.com

Norml
National organization advocating for cannabis legalization.
norml.org

Patients Out of Time
Provides information that help guide patients and caregivers
to make informed decisions.
Patientsoutoftime.com

Rick Simpson
Information on Rick Simpson and where to buy his books.
phoenixtears.ca

Dr. Dustin Sulak
Webinars, latest studies, information, and dosage guidance.
Healer.com

Podcasts

Hausman, Oscar and Wise, Jonny. "Dr David (Dedi) Meiri, Head of Laboratory for Cancer Biology & Cannabinoid Research, Technion-Israel Institute of Technology." Professionally Cannabis & Psychedelics, Global Cannabis Intelligence, August 24, 2022.

Weil, M.D., Andrew and Maizes, M.D., Victoria. "Medical Cannabis with Dr. Ethan Russo." Body of Wonder, Episode #14, Andrew Weil Center for Integrative Medicine at the University of Arizona, January 14, 2021.

Books

Desai, Panache. *Discovering Your Soul Signature: A 33-Day Path to Purpose, Passion & Joy*. Random House, New York, NY. 2014.

Simpson, Rick. *Rick Simpson Oil – Nature's Answer for Cancer*. Simpson RamaDur d.o.o., Jurja Dobrile 20, 10000 Zagreb, Croatia. 2013.

Weil, M.D., Andrew. *Spontaneous Healing*. Ballantine Books, New York, NY. 2000.

Werner, Clint. *Marijuana Gateway to Health*. Dachstar Press, San Francisco, CA. 2011.

ABOUT KELLY'S OIL

Kelly's Oil is a true adventure story about putting everything on the line to strike out to find a cure for Kelly's brain tumor. It is also a love story between Kelly and her devoted husband, Rick, and a family story about the power of friendship and connection.

Kelly's Oil is also a tacit indictment of federal laws, meager funding, and social deterrents preventing research into mainstream medicinal potentials of marijuana, one of Earth's most complex and beneficial plants.

CPSIA information can be obtained
at www.ICGtesting.com
Printed in the USA
JSHW052357011222
34009JS00004B/21